D1126503

258
259

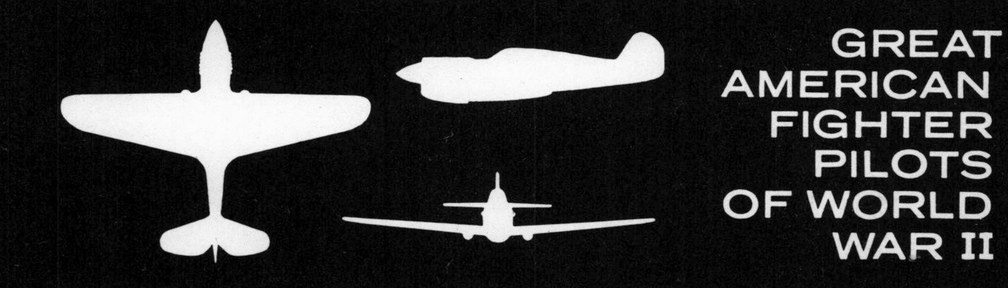
GREAT
AMERICAN
FIGHTER
PILOTS
OF WORLD
WAR II

RANDOM HOUSE · NEW YORK

GREAT AMERICAN FIGHTER PILOTS OF WORLD WAR II

By **Robert D. Loomis**

ILLUSTRATED WITH PHOTOGRAPHS

 Published in New York by Random House, Inc., and simultaneously in Toronto, Canada, by Random House of Canada, Limited.

Library of Congress Catalog Card Number: 61-7780

Manufactured in the United States of America

Contents

For Gloria

Foreword

The word ace, as applied to fighter pilots, grew out of an unofficial title given in World War I to a flier who had met and vanquished five or more enemy aircraft in aerial combat. The name originated with the French, who used the term "l'as," their word for the highest card in the deck.

As Robert Loomis so effectively shows in this book, American fighter pilots were certainly not cut from the same cloth. As different as they were individually, however, they did have a few things in common, especially a sheer love of flying. Moreover, most of the good ones seemed to blossom out under the leadership of other good ones. Such examples apparently set up a kind of chain reaction.

But if there is one word which best describes all the great aces, that word is aggressive. The defensive pilot, no matter how good a flier or how accurately he could hit a target on the home range, seemed to score few victories. Study a cross section of fighter pilots and you will discover that a startlingly small group of the very top aces (men such as Bong, Foss, McCampbell, McGuire, Gabreski, Blakeslee, Meyer, Schilling) accounted for an overwhelmingly large percentage of all enemy planes. As you will see in "Great American Fighter Pilots of World War II," the highest scores went to the men who relentlessly searched out the enemy regardless of the existing orders or the obstacles, and then pressed the attack, no matter what the odds. It was this special attitude which inspired that most descriptive name of all for the jet fighter pilot in Korea—"tiger."

As we enter this age of missiles it is highly probable that the fighter pilot is as out of date as the celebrated Knights of the Round Table. But like those earlier knights, the fighter ace too will pass into history and legend, for the story of what he did is well worth remembering.

Robert Lee Scott, Jr.

Robert Lee Scott, Jr.
B/Gen., USAF(ret.)

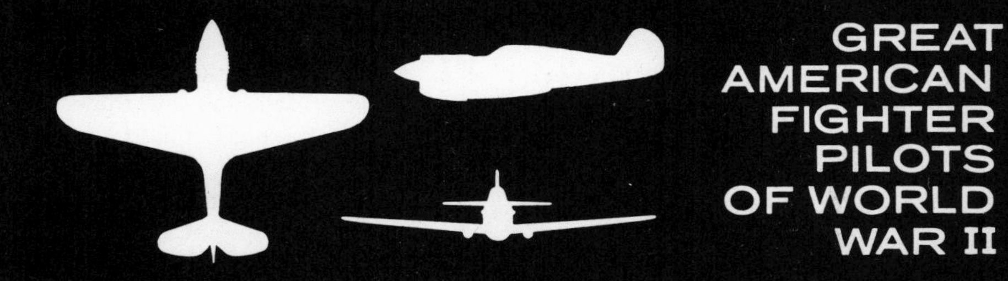
GREAT
AMERICAN
FIGHTER
PILOTS
OF WORLD
WAR II

MITSUBISHI ZERO

1 Days of Infamy

At exactly 7:55 on a beautiful Sunday morning the United States was suddenly plunged into the greatest conflict in the history of the world. We were not only unprepared for war, but our armed forces in the Pacific were caught completely by surprise.

That same Sunday morning two young Army Air Corps lieutenants were just leaving an all-night party at Wheeler Field, Hawaii. They were George Welsh and Ken Taylor of the 15th Pursuit Group. As they stood outside an army barracks watching the tropical dawn grow brighter, neither had any idea of the momentous event which was about to change their lives. It was December 7,

1941. Welsh was saying that instead of going to sleep, he wanted to drive back to their own base at nearby Haleiwa Field for a nice Sunday morning swim.

At that moment, just ten miles south of Lieutenants Welsh and Taylor, carrier-based dive bombers, torpedo planes and fighters of the Imperial Japanese Navy were beginning their carefully planned sneak attack on the great American naval base at Pearl Harbor, as well as its surrounding airfields. Most of our powerful Pacific Fleet was in training, and there were ninety-six United States warships anchored in and about this Pacific stronghold. War had been expected by our military leaders, but the general opinion was that the Japanese would open hostilities against the Dutch or British possessions in Asia thousands of miles farther west.

As Welsh and Taylor walked to their car to head back to their own base, they saw sixty-two new Curtiss P-40 "Tomahawks" parked wing tip to wing tip so they could be guarded "against sabotage."

Suddenly the Japanese swooped down on Wheeler Field, which was a center for fighter operations in Hawaii. Dive bombers seemed to appear out of nowhere. Violent explosions upended the parked planes, and buildings began to burn.

U.S. battleships aflame after the attack on Pearl Harbor

Welsh ran for a telephone and called Haleiwa as bullets sprayed around him.

"Get two P-40s ready!" he yelled. "It's not a gag—the Japs are here."

The drive up to Haleiwa was a wild one. Japanese Zeros strafed Welsh and Taylor three times. When the two fliers careened onto their field nine minutes later, their fighter planes were already armed and the propellers were turning over. Without waiting for orders they took off.

As they climbed for altitude they ran into twelve Japanese Val dive bombers over the Marine air base at Ewa. Welsh and Taylor began their attack immediately. On their first pass, machine guns blazing, each shot down a bomber. As Taylor zoomed up and over in his Tomahawk he saw an enemy bomber heading out to sea. He gave his P-40 full throttle and roared after it. Again his aim was good and the Val broke up before his eyes. In the meantime Welsh's plane had been hit and he dived into a protective cloud bank. The damage didn't seem too serious so he flew out again—only to find himself on the tail of another Val. With only one gun now working he nevertheless managed to send the bomber flaming into the sea.

Both pilots now vectored toward burning Wheeler Field for more ammunition and gas. Unfortunately the extra cartridge belts for the P-40s were in a hangar which was on fire. Two mechanics ran bravely into the dangerous inferno and returned with the ammunition.

The Japanese were just beginning a second strafing of the field as Welsh and Taylor hauled their P-40s into the air again. They headed directly into the enemy planes, all guns firing. This time Ken Taylor was hit in the arm, and then a Val closed in behind him. Welsh kicked his rudder and

Damaged hangar at Pearl Harbor

the Tomahawk whipped around and blasted the Val, though his own plane had been hit once more. Taylor had to land, but George Welsh shot down still another bomber near Ewa before he returned.

Perhaps twenty American fighter planes managed to get into the air that morning—including five obsolete Republic P-35s. Most of them were shot down, but their bravery and initiative accounted for six victories in the one-sided aerial battle.

The United States possessed no airplane which could outfight the Japanese Zero on its own terms. The Zero was faster—except in a dive. It could outturn the American fighter planes and it could outclimb them. It was the most important weapon Japan had until the Kamikaze planes were intro-

Japanese Zero fighter captured by American forces

duced near the end of the war. At first our pilots did not know the weaknesses of the Zero—that it had no armor, that it had no self-sealing gasoline tanks, and that its explosive 20-mm. cannons did not have the range or accuracy of the smaller but powerful .50-caliber machine guns mounted in our newest fighters. Also our pilots had not yet perfected the principle of the wingman, who was trained to stick close to his leader during combat and protect him from any attack from the rear.

Admiral Isoroku Yamamoto, who was in charge of all Japanese naval operations, had planned the Pearl Harbor strike brilliantly. In a few hours all of the Navy and Marine aircraft at Ewa air base were destroyed on the ground. Two-thirds of the Pacific Fleet was either sunk or seriously crippled. Luckily our two aircraft carriers in the South Pacific, the *Lexington* and the *Enterprise,* were away from Pearl Harbor during the attack.

The Japanese particularly wanted to catch our carriers in the harbor. Admiral Yamamoto knew the value of the carrier better than most naval commanders. As early as 1915 he had stated that: "The most important ship of the future will be a ship to carry airplanes." (After the war we learned that most of the messages sent from Pearl Harbor by a Japanese spy had to do with the whereabouts of our carriers.)

The *Enterprise* didn't escape entirely, however. She was on her way back to Pearl Harbor after delivering Major Paul Putnam's squadron of Marine Grumman F4F "Wildcats" to Wake Island. Heavy seas had kept the "Big E" from arriving on

time—which would have meant her destruction. But many of her scouts and bombers which flew in ahead of the ship were caught in the initial Japanese attack, and five were lost.

Even more tragic was the fate suffered by Navy Lieutenant Fritz Hebel. He was leading his Wildcat fighters from the *Enterprise* toward Ford Island in Pearl Harbor later that day after completing a search mission. It was 7:30 and getting dark. The men on the ground were still jittery from the morning attacks. As Hebel's fighters came in for a landing the whole sky suddenly filled with tracer bullets. Practically every ship in the harbor thought the Wildcats were Japanese planes returning for another raid. Lieutenant Hebel and three other Navy pilots were killed by our own guns.

Invasion of the Philippines

Approximately 4,000 miles due west of Pearl Harbor lie the Philippine Islands. At the time of the Japanese attack, America had many important military installations on these islands, especially airfields. Our most vital bases were on Luzon, the northernmost island in the group, and Luzon was only 600 miles away from powerful enemy airfields on Formosa.

The Japanese knew their bombers could easily

Captured Japanese photograph showing an enemy carrier during the attack on Pearl Harbor fly this distance and back, but they also knew American fighter planes in the Philippines would be alerted by the news from Hawaii. Therefore the Japanese bombers would need protection. This was where the versatile Zero again played an important part in the Japanese plans. By now the Zero pilots had learned how to keep the plane in the air an amazing ten to twelve hours and fly it up to 1400 miles nonstop.

As at Pearl Harbor, fate seemed to be on the side of the attackers. When the warning was flashed to Philippine headquarters, P-40s at Iba Field took off immediately to intercept the expected Japanese bombers and fighters. But unknown to the Americans, the enemy had been held up by bad weather. When the Japanese did make their first strike it was at an unlikely place named Baguio, the summer capital. Our planes had either been sent to protect the wrong targets or were already back on the ground.

The major and most devastating raids came approximately two hours later, at 11:30, when the Japanese struck Iba and Clark fields. At Iba our P-40s were coming back after the first attack, out of fuel and unprepared. They had downed one bomber but had lost eight fighters, and many more were destroyed on the ground.

It was Clark Field, however, that proved to be

the real disaster—it was later called "Little Pearl Harbor."

The largest four-engine bombing force in the world—twenty-two new Boeing B-17 "Flying Fortresses"—was sitting on the field. Most of the B-17s were destroyed as seventy-five Japanese bombers roared overhead, strafing and bombing. Only four P-40s managed to get into the air. Lieutenant Randall Keaton skillfully machine-gunned two of the attackers and was credited with the first official air "kill" in the bitter battle for Luzon. The slow old-fashioned P-35s ordered to Clark from Del Carmen arrived too late, as did the P-40s of the 17th Pursuit Squadron led by a pilot who was to become one of the most famous in the Philippines, Lieutenant Edward Dyess. It wasn't Dyess' fault he missed the interception. The radio station, along with almost everything else, had been wiped out at Clark Field.

By December 10th we had only twenty-two P-40s and eight P-35s left in the Philippines. Sometimes as many as 150 Zeros would accompany the Japanese bombers, and American fighter planes simply couldn't cope with them. On this same day the Japanese made small landings in the north at Aparri and Vigan, and General MacArthur ordered that our remaining fighters be used mostly for observation.

Despite this order, the most courageous exploits of our fighter pilots were yet to come. On the very next day, December 11th, Lieutenant Boyd D. "Buzz" Wagner took off on a hazardous one-man reconnaissance mission over the landings at Aparri. Wagner became the first American fighter pilot to shoot down five enemy planes in the Pacific, and therefore he became our first ace in World War II. He was called "Buzz" because, according to his buddies, he could *buzz* the camouflage off a hanger roof.

As he flew over Aparri, Wagner couldn't resist going down lower to strafe, and he was jumped by five Zeros. Rolling over, Wagner dived for the sea, but he couldn't shake the two Zeros which followed. Suddenly he chopped his power. The two speedy Zeros roared past him. He kicked his rudder hard right and then left, machine guns blazing. Both Zeros burst into flames. Coming back toward Aparri, flying low over the water, "Buzz" surprised the Japanese on the ground. He strafed twelve parked Zeros with murderous accuracy, leaving five of them burning hulks.

A few days later Wagner led a flight of three P-40s against an enemy-held field at Vigan. He ripped up the field first with 30-pound fragmentation bombs. Then Lieutenant Russell Church, coming right behind Wagner, was hit by ground fire.

Nevertheless Church bravely continued his attack, guns chattering, until he crashed.

Wagner returned to avenge Church. Recklessly he made five low-level passes at the field, not only destroying several planes but also setting fire to a fuel dump. A Zero tried to take off right under Wagner. Buzz couldn't see exactly where the enemy fighter was so he flipped into a half roll, then back, and waited until the Japanese pilot flew into his sights. Then Wagner touched the trigger. His .30-caliber slugs chewed the Zero to pieces.

On December 22nd the main Japanese invasion force of 43,000 landed at Lingayen Gulf only 100 miles north of Manila. They could not be contained. Slowly, courageously, MacArthur's stubborn forces withdrew toward Bataan Peninsula across the bay from Manila.

The Ordeal of Wake Island

In a remote spot in the vast Pacific Ocean another courageous battle was reaching a climax. Almost halfway between Hawaii and the Philippines sits a tiny wishbone-shaped atoll named Wake Island. Garrisoned by approximately 500 officers and men, mostly marines, Wake was also on the Japanese timetable for conquest. Again

CHINA
JAPAN
TOKYO
OKINAWA
IWO JIMA
FORMOSA
THE PHILIPPINE ISLANDS
P A C I F I
APARRI
VIGAN
LINGAYEN GULF
BAGUIO
LUZON
CLARK FIELD
SUBIC BAY
MANILA
BATAAN
SAN BERNARDINO STRAIT
TACLOBAN
DULAG
LEYTE GULF
ORMOC
LEYTE
ORMOC BAY
SURIGAO STRAIT
CEBU
MARIANA ISLANDS
SAIPAN
TINIAN
GUAM
ENIW
TRUK
HOLLANDIA
NEW IRELAND
NEW BRITAIN
RABAUL
NEW GUINEA
LAE
SALAMAUA
BUNA
PORT MORESBY
BOUGAINVILLE
"THE SLOT"
VELLA LAVELLA
MUNDA
NEW GEORGIA
TULAGI
GUADALCANAL
SOLOMON ISLANDS
CORAL SE
AUSTRALIA

THE PACIFIC ISLAND GROUPS

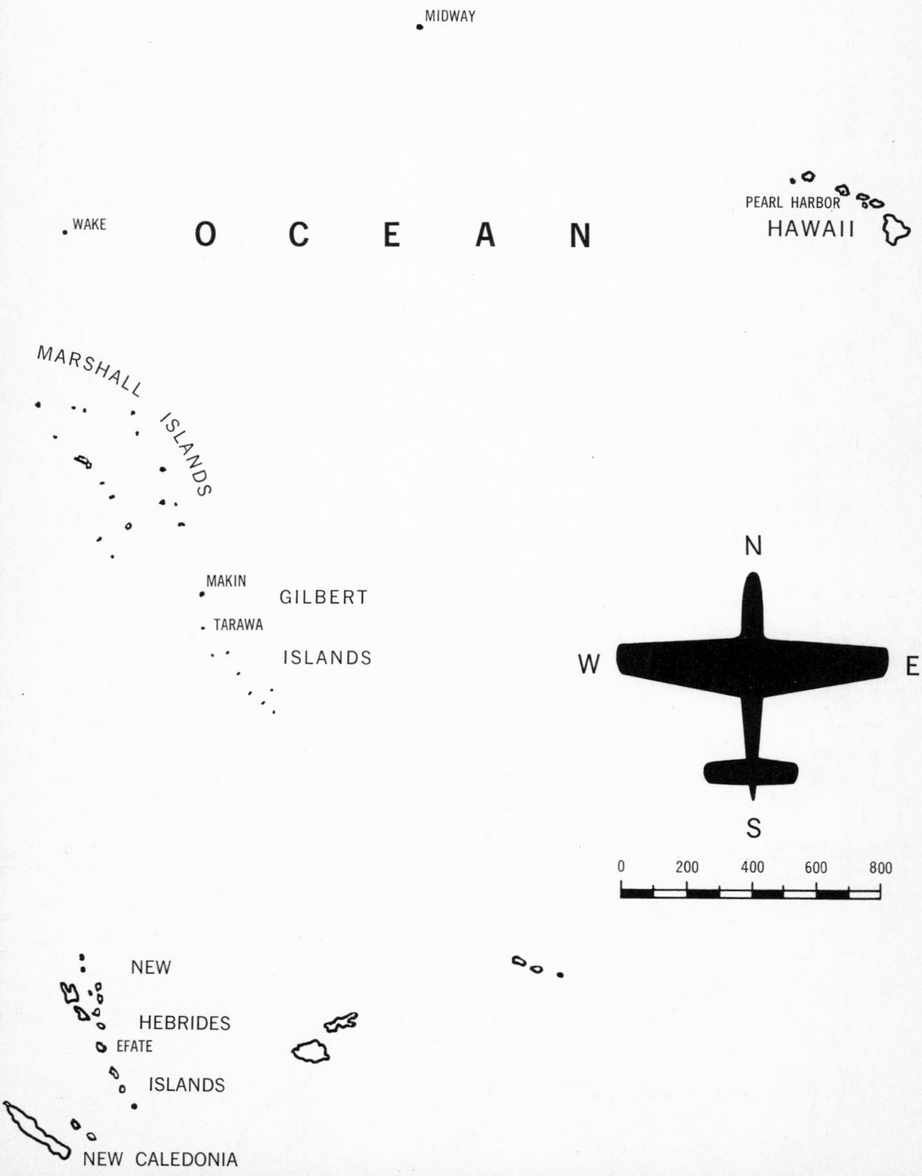

MIDWAY

WAKE

OCEAN

PEARL HARBOR

HAWAII

MARSHALL ISLANDS

MAKIN

GILBERT

TARAWA

ISLANDS

N

W

E

S

0 200 400 600 800

NEW

HEBRIDES

EFATE

ISLANDS

NEW CALEDONIA

actual invasion was planned.

Major Paul Putnam had led his twelve Marine Grumman F4F Wildcats from the deck of the *Enterprise* to Wake on December 4th. These blue, stubby Wildcats were new to his pilots and completely unfamiliar to the mechanics on the tiny island. Even with Putnam's squadron, the Wake defenders knew it would be almost impossible to prepare for coming attacks. They had no radar, and little hope that further reinforcements would reach them.

A few hours after the initial wave of bombers struck Pearl Harbor, thirty-six Japanese Betty bombers came in undetected from the south and blasted Wake. Eight of Putnam's Wildcats were destroyed. But the four that were left put up a gallant fight which helped delay the final capture of the island for two weeks.

The next day the four Wildcats were waiting for the Bettys. They shot down one, and others were damaged by anti-aircraft fire. On December 10th Captain Henry "Baron" Elrod destroyed two more enemy bombers in a vicious fight over the island.

Late that night a Japanese landing force approached Wake. Major James Devereux, the Marine commander, withheld his shore batteries until the Japanese force was only 4500 yards away. Then he let go with every gun on Wake Island.

A destroyer was sunk—the first Japanese warship to be sent to the bottom in the war—and several other ships were hit.

In the meantime Major Putnam's four Wildcats, armed with 100-pound bombs, were bearing down on the retreating ships. The little fighter planes flew out again and again—ten times in all—to attack this fleet of three cruisers, six destroyers and several transports. One of Captain Elrod's bombs scored a direct hit on the destroyer *Kisaragi,* and then he and Lieutenant Frank "Duke" Therin raked the doomed ship with their machine guns. It is not known how many hundreds of enemy sailors and assault troops were killed by the fighter pilots of Putnam's squadron, but Japanese Admiral Kajioka gave credit where credit was due. In his diary he wrote: "Dec. 11—Wake Island landing after sunset unsuccessful because of fighter plane opposition."

Without reinforcements the fall of Wake was only a matter of time. Yet the strength of the resistance was so upsetting to the Japanese that Yamamoto ordered the man who led the force which attacked Pearl Harbor, Admiral Nagumo, to take his 2nd Carrier Division to Wake.

The next morning, December 12th, the Wildcat pilots attacked thirty more Betty bombers, even though only two Grummans were still in flyable

F4F Wildcat fighter plane

condition. Each day the fighters took off to intercept, and each day the mechanics on the ground patched them up, using engines and propellers from other damaged F4Fs.

Then, on December 22nd, the inevitable happened. Japanese bombers arrived over Wake with an escort of agile Zero fighters. Captain Herbert Freuler blasted one of the Zeros out of the sky, but soon his plane was hit, as was the other, last remaining Wildcat on Wake.

The few survivors of Putnam's squadron now became infantrymen. Just after midnight on the twenty-third of December, the Japanese finally landed on Wake. The fighting was brief but furious. Major Putnam was shot through the jaw. Elrod was killed while throwing a hand grenade. By sundown on December 24th, Christmas Eve, the American flag had been lowered on Wake Island. Its gallant defenders received the first Presidential citation of the war, but they knew nothing about it until five years later when they were released by the defeated Japanese. Captain Elrod was posthumously awarded the Congressional Medal of Honor.

The Fall of Bataan

Christmas Day in the Philippines was not a happy one either. Thousands of Americans and Filipinos were retreating into Bataan Peninsula on Luzon. Our remaining P-40s were sent to two small airstrips being readied on the Peninsula. Some of the fighter pilots were put into the infantry. There were no planes for them to fly, and no place to fly from.

Ed Dyess—now a captain—was one of these pilots. They gathered an odd assortment of weapons, including guns salvaged from crushed P-40s and fitted with homemade mounts. Around the middle of January, Dyess helped drive off a new Japanese invasion attempt on the west coast of Bataan itself.

As soon as the new bases were ready at Cabcaben and Bataan airfields, General Harold H. "Pursuit" George called Dyess and his men back to the 21st Squadron. At Bataan Field, Dyess found just five P-40s still in flyable condition. A few battered civilian planes called the "Bamboo Fleet"—an old biplane, a Beechcraft, a Bellanca, a Waco, and a Navy "Duck" salvaged from the waters around Bataan—tried to bring in supplies and evacuate important people. Dyess and his fellow pilots had little food left. Their fields were sometimes under direct fire from infiltrating Japanese jungle troops. The pilots often ate monkeys, lizards and anything else they could shoot.

On March 2nd the Japanese were reported making a landing in Subic Bay on the northwest coast of Bataan. Dyess, who called his P-40 *Kibosh*, got permission from General George to attack the invaders with 500-pound bombs. On his first mission he missed with his bomb, but sprayed the ships and barges with .50-caliber slugs. Loading up again, he dive-bombed a freighter from 10,000 feet. Pulling out at 2,000 he hit it squarely. Debris and smoke mushroomed gloriously. Again *Kibosh*

William E. Dyess (Army Air Forces)

strafed the area. On his third mission Dyess hit an enormous supply dump on an island in the middle of the Bay. Then with his six machine guns he attacked a transport slipping out of Subic Bay. Incredibly this ship caught fire and it too blew up. The Bay was a holocaust. Later the Japanese claimed it had been raided by three flights of four-engine bombers.

The other fighter pilots had been carrying the fight to the enemy too, but by the end of the day Ed Dyess' *Kibosh* was the only P-40 left on Bataan.

On April 9th Bataan surrendered. The last

flight out was made in the Navy "Duck" piloted by Captain Roland Barnick. Dyess was supposed to go along but refused. Five passengers, including Carlos Romulo, packed themselves into the amphibian which was meant to carry only two. The battered "Duck" could climb to an altitude of only seventy-five feet, even when those aboard threw out everything—the floorboards, their clothing and baggage. The plane managed to get to Cebu without instruments.

Ed Dyess along with thousands of other Americans went to Marivelles Airfield, where he surrendered. Of course many Americans managed to escape to Corregidor Island, which succumbed a month later, and some got to Australia. Buzz Wagner, for instance, had been wounded in the eye and was sent out—too late—to ferry P-40s back to Bataan.

The story of Bataan is an unusually courageous one, and the P-40 and her brave pilots wrote a particularly memorable chapter in the history of fighting men. After the war, General Henry "Hap" Arnold said: "But for the P-40 the Japanese would have come all the way to Australia."

F4F WILDCAT

2 Struggle for the Sea

The role of the fighter pilot aboard an aircraft carrier at sea is the same as that of a fighter pilot anywhere: to win and hold control of the air. Until he does this, his own base—the carrier—is not safe. And the important bombers and torpedo planes the ship carries may not be able to get through the enemy fighter screens with their lethal loads.

To be successful, the fighter pilot had to master more tasks than any other single man in World War II. He had to be exceptionally good, of course, at handling a fighter plane—alert, with superior coördination and split-second timing. There was an unprecedented amount of technical

F4F Wildcat landing on flight deck of carrier

know-how to absorb, including complex mechanical systems, electronics, navigation, radio and operational procedures. He had to be a good shot, too. All of this called for unusual judgment, skill and courage.

The Saga of Butch O'Hare

Nothing could dramatize these qualities better—or illustrate their value more vividly—than the heroic exploits of Navy Lieutenant Edward "Butch" O'Hare on February 20, 1942. The carrier *Lexington* had been assigned the dangerous task of penetrating enemy-held waters north of

New Ireland. From there her planes were to make a strike at Japanese shipping in the harbor at Rabaul. Unfortunately, while still 400 miles from Rabaul, the *Lexington* was discovered by a giant four-engine Kawanishi flying boat. Lieutenant Commander John Thach, skipper of the *Lexington's* Wildcat fighters, shot down the Japanese "snooper," but not before it had radioed the carrier's position.

That afternoon Commander Thach led six Wildcats into the air to intercept nine twin-engine enemy bombers. In a determined attack each of the Wildcats destroyed a bomber and damaged two more. The ship's anti-aircraft guns finished off the rest.

In the meantime, nine more Japanese bombers were reported on the way. Six Wildcats, one of them piloted by Butch O'Hare, roared off the *Lexington's* deck to stop them. O'Hare and his wingman spotted the V formation of bombers first and dived to try to head them off. The other F4F pilots were too far away to reach most of the enemy planes before they released their bombs.

As if this weren't bad enough, O'Hare's wingman discovered his guns were jammed. He was forced to turn away. Butch O'Hare stood alone between the *Lexington* and the bombers.

O'Hare didn't hesitate. Full throttle, he roared

Edward H. O'Hare (Navy)

into the enemy formation. While tracers from the concentrated fire of the nine bombers streaked around him, he took careful aim at the starboard engine of the last plane in the V and squeezed his trigger. Slugs from the Wildcat's six .50-caliber guns ripped into the Japanese bomber's wing and the engine literally jumped out of its mountings. The bomber spun crazily toward the sea as O'Hare's guns tore up another enemy plane. Then he ducked to the other side of the formation and smashed the port engine of the last Japanese plane there.

One by one he attacked the oncoming bombers until five had been downed. Commander Thach later reported that at one point he saw three of the bombers falling in flames at the same time.

By now Thach and the other pilots had joined the fight. This was lucky because O'Hare was out of ammunition. The Wildcats took care of several more bombers and the *Lexington* managed to evade the few bombs that were released.

It was an amazing example of daring and shooting skill. Afterward Thach figured out that Butch O'Hare had used only sixty rounds of ammunition for each plane he destroyed. He had probably saved his ship. He was promoted to lieutenant commander and awarded the highest decoration of his country, the Congressional Medal of Honor.

First Blood—The Coral Sea

By late April, 1942, the first important sea battle between American and Japanese forces was shaping up. In March, planes from the *Enterprise* had hit Japanese-occupied Wake Island, and the *Lexington* teamed with the *Yorktown* to strike enemy bases at Lae and Salamaua on New Guinea, a large island just off the northern coast of Australia.

Intelligence reports indicated that the Japanese were planning to invade Port Moresby near the eastern tip of New Guinea. The enemy task force intended to sail around this eastern tip into the Coral Sea and then attack.

Port Moresby was vital to Allied strategy. From it we based our campaign in New Guinea. If Port Moresby were lost, Australia would be threatened.

The *Lexington* and *Yorktown* were ordered into the Coral Sea to intercept the invaders.

At 10:30 A.M. on May 5th, the two carriers heard a report from Lieutenant Commander James Flatley, who led the *Yorktown's* fighters. At the moment he was flying on combat air patrol (CAP) overhead, and he had spotted a Kawanishi flying boat spying on the task force.

"Where is he?" the *Lexington* wanted to know.

"Wait a minute and I'll show you," radioed Flatley.

Suddenly there was an explosion, and a great ball of fire tumbled from the clouds. It was the Kawanishi falling. Jimmy Flatley's guns had scored a hit.

On its way down, the big plane almost struck Lieutenant Noel Gayler's Wildcat. Gayler was off the *Lexington*.

"Hey, Jimmy," he yelled, "that one almost hit me."

"That'll teach you to fly underneath me when Japs are around," Flatley quipped. As a matter of fact Flatley was "around" only by chance himself. A few days before, he had been ordered back to the States to form a new fighter squadron, but he managed to get permission to stay for the coming battle.

On the morning of May 7th, a scout from the *Lexington* reported an enemy carrier, the *Shoho,* 180 miles away. Ninety-three planes—dive bombers, torpedo planes and fighters—were sent to the attack. In less than an hour our planes found the *Shoho* and her escorts and the first bombers were nosing over into screaming dives from an altitude of 15,000 feet. Within a half hour the *Shoho* was a sinking inferno.

The men on the *Lexington* heard an excited report from Commander Bob Dixon in one of the scout bombers over the target: "Scratch one flattop!"

American fliers had sunk the first carrier to be lost by either side. As a matter of fact, it was the first important warship we had destroyed.

Later that same day four Wildcats from both the *Lexington* and the *Yorktown* attacked a formation of nine Zeros flying overhead and shot down seven of them. In this fight Jimmy Flatley got three.

That night there occurred one of the strangest incidents of the war at sea. In the darkness a formation of Japanese bombers tried to land on the

Lexington, mistaking it for one of their own carriers. Immediately the *Lexington's* guns came to life, and red tracers crisscrossed through the night. Eleven of the bombers crashed into the sea. Actually their own fleet was only thirty miles away.

Just after dawn on the following day, two Japanese carriers—the *Shokaku* and the *Zuikaku*—were sighted. Immediately the United States carriers launched seventy-three aircraft. Lieutenant Noel Gayler was one of the fighter pilots escorting a flight of old Douglas TBD "Devastator" torpedo planes. He and three other pilots from the *Lexington* tore into the screen of Zeros protecting the Japanese carriers. The American fliers were heavily outnumbered but their courageous attack allowed the slow torpedo planes to get through. Gayler destroyed two of the Zeros and the other Wildcat pilots got one each. But only Gayler survived the fight. On his way back to the *Lexington,* Gayler discovered two Kawanishi flying boats in his path. With the last of his ammunition he shot them both down. Gayler was now the Navy's top ace with eight victories.

In the meantime, Japanese planes had found the American carriers. Unfortunately, most of our Wildcats were miles away escorting American bombers, so Lieutenant Stanley "Swede" Vejtasa's squadron of Douglas SBD "Dauntless" dive bomb-

Devastator torpedo bombers aboard American aircraft carrier, prior to their take-off for attack on Japanese carriers

ers was pressed into service to replace the missing fighter planes. They had to do their best to protect the *Lexington* and *Yorktown*. The Dauntless was at least 100 miles an hour slower than the Zero and had only two guns firing forward.

At 11:14 A.M. Vejtasa's six planes were jumped by twelve Zeros. Two Dauntlesses fell flaming into the water. Vejtasa managed to escape the first attack and yelled to his radio man: "Son, we're in for a scrap. Keep your head and conserve your ammunition. . . . I'll take care of the rest."

As the Zeros closed in again, Swede Vejtasa fought with the skill of a born fighter pilot. His rear gunner kept the swift Zeros off his flanks, while Vejtasa calmly leveled his sights at the Japanese fighters coming head on for the steady Dauntless. Again and again—three times—he maneuvered the scout bomber so that its two forward-firing guns ripped into a Zero. Three times a surprised Japanese pilot found himself spinning into the Coral Sea.

Another Dauntless pilot was proving he could handle the Zero too. Lieutenant John Leppla who, with his gunner D. K. Liska, had flamed four Japanese planes the day before during the bombing attack on the carrier *Shoho,* now put his newfound talent to work again. Without hesitation Leppla sent his Dauntless plunging into the deadly enemy torpedo planes heading for the *Lexington.* Not only did Leppla send three of these Japanese bombers careening into the water below but he also saved the life of a fellow Dauntless pilot by a daring attack on a Zero about to shoot down the American. (Later Commander Flatley picked outstanding bomber pilots like Swede Vejtasa and John Leppla to form his new fighter group, which would be named the "Grim Reapers.")

All in all it was quite a day in the air.

On the sea it was another matter. American

Aircraft carrier USS Lexington burning after the battle of the Coral Sea

planes had again broken through the Japanese fighter defenses and seriously damaged a second carrier, but the enemy planes had penetrated the weak Wildcat-Dauntless screen too. The *Lexington,* hit with five torpedoes, was doomed. The *Yorktown* was pounded by Japanese dive bombers, but her crew successfully fought the resulting fires.

Tactically the Battle of the Coral Sea was almost a draw. In fact you could say the United States lost it if you simply compared the number of ships sunk or damaged on each side. But the Japanese were forced to turn back from Port Moresby, and that was the important thing at the moment. It was also the first major fight at sea in which the ships involved neither saw nor shot at each other.

As the gallant *Lexington* began to sink, her crew was ordered to abandon her. Hundreds of men were already in the water when Noel Gayler decided he had better get off too. He jumped the fifty feet into the sea, and then some time later was seen climbing back up a rope to the flight deck of the badly listing ship. Dripping wet he stood calmly in front of a few of the nervous fighter pilots still aboard.

One of them asked him, "What did you come back for?"

Gayler's answer showed, if nothing else, his

calmness in battle. "Oh, I got a bit lonely out there," he said. "I didn't know any of those guys. When are you fellows going to come?"

Midway—The Turning Point

Even before the Battle of the Coral Sea, Admiral Yamamoto had devised a plan to destroy completely America's sea power in the Pacific. He wanted to attack and invade the island of Midway, which is just 1300 miles west of Pearl Harbor. Yamamoto figured the American fleet would steam to defend Midway. Then the Japanese fleet, which was far superior in numbers, could wipe it out. He also planned a smaller diversionary strike at the Aleutian Islands, which stretch out into the Pacific from Alaska.

What Yamamoto didn't know was that United States military intelligence officers had discovered the key to the Japanese secret code, and so we knew of their plans. Yamamoto also thought the *Yorktown* had been sunk in the Coral Sea. Actually she was badly damaged, but hard-working shipyard men in Pearl Harbor had accomplished the necessary repairs in two days—a job that ordinarily would have taken more than two months.

Yamamoto had assembled an imposing force. He sent six carriers, eleven battleships, sixteen cruisers and forty-five destroyers to converge on Midway. Against this giant fleet, Admiral Chester Nimitz had only three carriers—*Yorktown, Hornet* and *Enterprise*—nine cruisers and fifteen destroyers. Nimitz had also fortified Midway itself.

At 5:34 A.M. on June 4th, a Navy Catalina flying boat spotted the Japanese attack force and radioed: "Many enemy planes heading Midway." These were the carrier-based fighters and bombers which were to "soften up" the island before the planned invasion. There were twenty-eight Marine fighter planes on Midway under the command of Major Floyd B. Parks. Nineteen of these were old Brewster F2A "Buffalo" fighters. Immediately Major Parks took off with seven Buffalos and five Wildcats to intercept the enemy attacking force. The rest of the fighters were ordered up too, but held in reserve.

When Parks first spotted the enemy formation at 14,000 feet, he saw over 100 fighter planes and bombers. The Zero escort was beneath the bombers, apparently not expecting fighter opposition.

The Marine fighters peeled off and roared into the Vals, all guns blazing. Several of the Japanese bombers were hit, and dropped away toward the sea. But then the Zeros saw the Marine fighter planes and climbed to meet the Wildcats and sluggish Buffalos. The Marine pilots didn't have a chance. The dancing Zeros cut up the brave defenders. Not only were the marines heavily outnumbered, but their planes could not match the performance of the Japanese fighters.

In a vicious dogfight the Americans lost plane after plane. In Parks' group only two pilots lived. One of them was Captain Marion Carl. He destroyed one Zero on his first pass, but as he climbed for altitude again other Zeros got on his tail. He nosed over, rammed everything to the firewall—that is, he gave his Wildcat full power—and pulled away. A Wildcat could at least outdive a Zero. In this way Captain Carl managed to escape. On his way home he made another attack on three Zeros below him and sent one down, burning and out of control.

The rest of the Marine fighter planes joined Major Parks' fight, but to no avail. After the "all clear," the Midway radio called: "Fighters land, refuel by divisions. . . ." No fighters landed. Then came the call, "All fighters land and reservice." Only ten planes came back, and only two would ever fly again.

It was the heaviest loss the Marines suffered in a single air battle during the entire war. One of our pilots said bitterly afterward that the Buffalo "should be in Miami as a training plane."

Later that same morning at 10:24 dive bombers

from the *Enterprise* and *Yorktown* found the Japanese carriers refueling and rearming their aircraft. Our Devastator torpedo planes had almost all been destroyed by the Japanese fighter screen and the withering fire from the enemy carriers, but our dive bombers caught the enemy carriers off guard. The Dauntlesses nosed over and began their deadly attack. In minutes three enemy carriers were hit, and raging, uncontrollable fires swept through the ships.

Yamamoto's fleet had been dealt a crushing blow.

That afternoon American fliers found a fourth large enemy carrier and badly damaged it too, but our own fleet now came under attack. Lieutenant Elbert McCuskey took off from the *Yorktown* with three other Wildcat pilots and faced the attacking Japanese bombers. The four American fighter planes disrupted the enemy formation, which was guarded by Zeros, and McCuskey personally shot down three of the bombers. Later the same day he destroyed two Zeros escorting enemy torpedo planes. Both the *Enterprise* and the *Yorktown* were hit, however—the *Yorktown* so badly that she could not be saved. Lieutenant McCuskey had been stationed on the *Lexington* when she went down in the Coral Sea; now his second ship, the *Yorktown,* was doomed too. His one consolation was that he

Fire and damage on the USS Yorktown during the Battle of Midway

had blasted five of the enemy in one day.

The Japanese fleet, burning and defeated, turned away. It would never again venture into open battle that far from home waters.

Yamamoto's Aleutian attack fared better. Japanese troops were landed at Attu and Kiska, far out on the string of islands, and it took nine months to dislodge them. But here too the United States had a bit of luck. A new-model Zero fighter plane crashed near Alaska after motor failure. Its pilot was killed accidentally as he tried to land. We captured the Zero intact and were able to study first-hand its design and performance. As a result we were able to modify somewhat the design of a new Navy fighter, the Grumman F6F "Hellcat." Soon the Navy pilots would have a plane which could outfly and outshoot anything the enemy put into the air.

The Lightnings Arrive

The Japanese were firmly entrenched in northern New Guinea, just off Australia. Between the enemy and Port Moresby, on New Guinea's southern coast, lay the Owen-Stanley Mountains. Daily American fighters and bombers flew over these mountains to attack the Japanese positions.

In September of 1942 a new group of fighter pilots reported to General George Kenney in Australia. They had come to a strange world full of unfamiliar names. They soon learned that Rabaul on the island of New Britain, lying just east of New Guinea, was the stronghold of the Japanese forces in the South Pacific. And on New Guinea were other strong points with strange names like Buna, Lae and Salamaua.

But the Army pilots had brought something with them that would be equally strange—and also deadly—to the Japanese. It was a new fighter plane, the Lockheed P-38 "Lightning." The Light-

P-38 Lightning

P-39 Airacobra

Thomas J. Lynch
(Army Air Forces)

ning had two engines, twin tails and a remarkable range. It was faster than the Zero and, more important, it could outclimb it.

In December General Kenney's new pilots got their first real chance to show the Japanese what they could do in their Lightnings. Captain Thomas Lynch led twelve P-38s out of Port Moresby to intercept an approaching enemy formation. In Lynch's formation was a "bad boy" General Kenney had been forced to discipline back in the States. His name was Richard Bong and he

Boyd D. "Buzz" Wagner
(Army Air Forces)

had not only looped-the-loop around the Golden Gate Bridge in San Francisco but had then buzzed Market Street in his Lightning and waved at the stenographers staring in astonishment out of office windows. Though General Kenney had given him a stiff talking to, he knew that Dick Bong had the makings of a first-rate fighter pilot.

At 18,000 feet Lynch's P-38s dropped their belly tanks—which carried extra fuel—and attacked the Japanese Zeros and Vals heading over the Owen-Stanley Mountains. It was a wild fight. In eight minutes the new and inexperienced American pilots downed fifteen enemy fighters and bombers. Tom Lynch got two and so did Dick Bong, who was in his first combat.

Kenney wrote an excited letter to General Arnold in Washington. The new boys did a lot of things wrong, he told Arnold: "They opened up too far away and did entirely too much dog-fighting [but] right now morale in that squadron is so high it almost scares you."

America had still another new fighter plane in the Port Moresby area before the end of 1942. It was the sleek Bell P-39 "Airacobra." It did not prove suitable for high-level combat, but in the right hands the P-39 gave the Japanese a real headache. Lieutenant Colonel Buzz Wagner, the hero of the Philippines, led the first strafing mission in the new Airacobras. His flight of twelve was jumped by Zeros. Wagner led his inexperienced pilots in a running, low-level fight in which he downed three Zeros himself.

The tide had not yet turned in our favor in the Pacific air war, but the courage and bravery of our fighter pilots was unsurpassed. One true story which the men in the 17th Pursuit Squadron liked to tell illustrates this quality very well. A P-40 pilot became lost from his formation over Java. He ran into a group of eighteen Zeros and eighteen bombers. His comrades heard him yelling over his radio: "Hey, fellas. I've got about thirty-six of them cornered over here! Somebody come on over!"

P-40 TOMAHAWK

3 Tigers Still

Late in 1941, three months before the attack on Pearl Harbor, a group of young men left San Francisco in several Dutch ships bound for the Far East. They told fellow passengers they were businessmen or teachers, and some, like Gregory Boyington, were instructed to say they were clergymen.

Actually they were American pilots from the Army Air Corps, Navy and Marines on their way to China to become part of a flying foreign legion called the American Volunteer Group (AVG). China had been at war with Japan for almost four years, and from the beginning Japanese war planes had been able to bomb and strafe helpless Chinese cities at will. Finally, in desperation,

China asked a retired Air Corps captain, Claire Chennault, to form a Chinese air force.

Chennault probably understood the value of fighter planes as well as anyone else in the world. He believed that the fighter was the key to air power. Without such fighters the air could not be controlled, and bombers would be at the mercy of the enemy. This was at a time when more and more air officers were beginning to believe that an armed bomber could take care of itself.

Chennault had written a book on the subject, *The Role of Defensive Pursuit,* but the Army would not listen to his ideas. Now in China he had a chance to test them in actual combat, and there is reason to believe that Chennault himself shot down at least thirty Japanese planes before the AVG arrived. At first he had no modern planes for his tiny command, but early in 1941 a group of Americans sent him a gift of 100 Curtiss-Wright P-40 Tomahawks. He got pilots for them by "raiding"—unofficially—the American military services. Men like Bob Neale and David "Tex" Hill came to fly with him. In reality they were mercenaries, and were paid $600 a month, plus $500 for each Japanese plane they destroyed.

Chennault taught them everything he knew. He showed them the strong points of the P-40—and the weaknesses of the Zero. He repeated over and over again: *never* try to turn with a Zero. Always get above the enemy and try to hit him on the first pass. After that keep going. The Zero could not catch the P-40 in a dive.

The nose of each Tomahawk was painted with a grinning shark's mouth, and three squadrons were formed. They were nicknamed the "Adam and Eves," the "Panda Bears" and "Hell's Angels."

On December 19th the Japanese got the surprise of their lives. A group of their bombers were on their way to bomb Kunming Field. They were unaware that Chennault's group, soon to be known as the Flying Tigers, were now trained and ready for combat. Consequently the Japanese bombers were not escorted by fighters.

Chennault dispatched several Tigers to intercept over the field, and also sent fifteen more to catch the bombers on their way back home. The trap worked. Only four Japanese planes escaped. After that Zero fighters always accompanied the bombers, but it made no difference; Chennault had taught his Tigers well. On Christmas Day the Japanese sent over one hundred fighters and bombers. The Hell's Angels Squadron—all eighteen of them—clawed at the massive enemy formation and destroyed thirty-three.

The Flying Tigers didn't lose a plane.

Of course once in a while a new man would forget Chennault's careful instructions. Gregory Boyington, Flight Leader of the Adam and Eves, found himself doing all the wrong things in his first combat. He was sure he could dog-fight the Zero. But no matter how hard he hauled back on the stick of his Tomahawk, the Zero turned inside him and each time he saw tracers whipping past his head. He finally gave up in disgust, lucky to escape with his life. Boyington learned quickly, however, and before he left the Flying Tigers he had downed six Japanese planes.

At no time after that first fight did the Flying Tigers have more than fifty P-40s ready for combat. And sometimes the fitness of these few planes was doubtful. A reporter once asked Bob Neale why he hadn't made a Victory Roll over the field after a successful mission. "Confidentially," said Neale, "we can't roll 'em any more. If we tried it, they'd probably fall apart in our laps."

Until it was absorbed into the Army on July 4, 1942, the American Volunteer Group set a matchless record, officially destroying 299 enemy planes while losing only 8 of their own pilots in combat. There is little doubt that easily twice this many Japanese aircraft were actually shot down.

A Proud Tradition Continues

July 4th was the date set for the AVG pilots to transfer into the regular Army Air Corps. They were all to become members of the 23rd Fighter Group. It was soon obvious, however, that most of the veterans of the Flying Tigers wanted either to go home or to rejoin their original branch of the service. Boyington, for instance, reënlisted in the Marine Corps. A few, like Tex Hill, stayed on.

Luckily many pilots agreed to remain for a brief time to help the new Army fighter commander, Colonel Robert L. Scott, Jr., get the 23rd in shape.

Bob Scott's story is one of the classic tales of World War II. He had always wanted to be a fighter pilot, but when war came along he was told he was too old. He was training other pilots when he heard that some B-17 Flying Fortresses were being sent on a secret mission to the Far East. Scott volunteered, though he had never flown a B-17. He was sure the Fortresses would take him close to Chennault.

Originally the Fortresses were to bomb Japan from China and then fly on to the Philippines. (This was just before Lieutenant Colonel James Doolittle's B-25 raid on Tokyo from the deck of the carrier *Hornet.*) But the Philippines fell and the

B-17s had no place to land, so the mission was canceled at the last minute. Instead, Scott found himself flying supplies to Chennault from India over the high and dangerous Himalaya Mountains. In no time Bob Scott talked Chennault into letting him fly a P-40 to help protect the transport planes flying over "The Hump."

When he wasn't escorting the transports, of course, the P-40 was his to do with as he pleased. On his own Scott began a one-man war against the Japanese on the Burma Road. He even had the propeller spinner on his Tomahawk, which he named *Old Exterminator,* painted a different color each day so the Japanese would think that a whole squadron of planes was strafing them. On some days he flew as many as five missions. When he could, Bob Scott also flew combat missions as a wingman with the Flying Tigers. It was one of the proudest moments of his life when Chennault picked him to lead the new 23rd Fighter Group.

When Colonel Scott led his fighters into combat for the first time on July 4th, the Japanese did not know that the experienced AVG fliers were still with him. The Zero pilots were all set to teach the new, inexperienced Americans a lesson. Instead, it was the same old story. Within minutes, thirteen Zeros fell from the skies, victims of the hot guns of the P-40s.

General Claire Chennault (Army Air Forces)

Robert L. Scott, Jr. (Army Air Forces)

Bob Scott receiving the Silver Star
from General Chennault

Scott's biggest day in combat came on October 23, 1942. With six other P-40s, he was escorting B-25 bombers raiding important shipyards in Victoria Harbor, Hong Kong. The B-25s were attacked by dozens of Zeros, and Scott rolled *Old Exterminator* on her back and headed for the lead plane. He began to squeeze his trigger while he was at least 1,000 yards away, but Tex Hill beat him to the enemy fighter. Then Scott turned his six .50-calibers on the next Zero and sent it spinning toward the harbor in flames. After that he got another Zero as it was just about to destroy a P-40. Often *Old Exterminator* would fall into a spin when Scott tried to pull it into too tight a turn, but he always recovered and climbed back into the fight. He exploded another Zero as it tried to attack the American bombers after they had finished their run. Now more enemy fighters were rising from the ground to help. These were twin-engine Messerschmitts. Scott nosed over and headed directly for the leader. The Messerschmitt tried to escape but couldn't get away. It too crashed into the water.

Afterward Scott couldn't resist strafing the penthouse of the Peninsular Hotel in Kowloon. This was enemy headquarters. On his way back home alone he was jumped by Zeros angry at the defeat just suffered by their fellow pilots. A cannon shell exploded just behind his armor plate. Fragments ripped into his back. He just managed to evade his pursuers by diving for the ground and weaving his way through the hills of Kwansi Province.

Before Colonel Scott was sent back to the States in January of 1943 he had been officially credited with shooting down thirteen Japanese planes.

Major John Alison was one of the new Army pilots to report for duty in the 23rd Fighter Group. In late July of 1942 he was sent to Hengyang Field, where Tex Hill was then commanding officer. The first action Alison experienced was a Japanese bombing attack at night. It made him mad and frustrated to be stuck on the ground just because of the dark. Then suddenly he had an idea. Why not take off anyway as soon as the Chinese warning net said a raid was coming, and be waiting overhead for the Japanese? He was sure he could find the bombers by looking for the bright exhaust flames from their motors.

Alison got enthusiastic support for his idea from Captain Albert "Ajax" Baumler, who had been an ace in the Spanish Civil War. It was Ajax who had once astounded Bob Scott by flying into combat a P-40 which was not only badly damaged but also had such a short in its electrical system that Baumler suffered severe shocks all through the flight. "I'll go with you," said Baumler, even though he knew as well as Alison that the P-40 was not equipped for night fighting.

On July 29th, Alison, Baumler and several other pilots who liked the idea waited far into the evening for the expected bombing attack. At 2:00

Left to right: John R. Alison, David L. "Tex" Hill and Albert J. "Ajax" Baumler (Army Air Forces)

A.M. the warning system reported bombers on the way. The fliers raced for their P-40s and one by one they roared off down the unlighted field and then climbed into the blackness overhead.

At 12,000 feet Alison tried to contact Hengyang, but all he could hear was static. Suddenly the static cleared for a moment and he heard: ". . .

three twin-engine bandits just went over the field . . ."

Alison couldn't pick out any planes on either side of him. Then he looked up. "I see them," he yelled into his microphone, as he rammed his throttle forward. "They're above me!" Ajax Baumler heard too and began to climb.

When Alison began his attack on the bombers, he discovered he was silhouetted between the moon and the Japanese. Therefore he presented a clear target himself. Though he felt his P-40 rock with explosions from the bombers' guns, he pressed his attack. His instrument panel was smashed, but now he could see that his own machine guns were ripping into the dark shape in front of him. Suddenly there was an explosion. He had hit the bomber's wing tank.

In the meantime Baumler also had a bomber in flames. But there was another enemy bomber left and it was about to drop its high explosive. By now Alison's P-40 was smoking, and its engine was almost shaking itself from its mounts. Nevertheless Alison pressed on, firing his last ammunition at the bomber. He saw pieces fly from the big plane's wing root, followed by a spurt of flame. Then down it went.

Alison couldn't get back to Hengyang. His engine quit and he crash-landed in the Siang

River. The next day he discovered that Ajax Baumler had shot down still another bomber. That made a total of four enemy ships downed in the first night operation—and no P-40s were lost because Alison's ship was pulled out of the river by the Chinese and flown again.

When Bob Scott left the outfit, he handed over command to Colonel Bruce Holloway. Holloway, like Scott, turned out to be not only a good fighter but an excellent leader as well.

On June 15, 1943, he and the 23rd gave the Japanese such a beating that they didn't come back for months. That day Holloway and three other pilots took off from Kunming when enemy planes were reported heading their way. The four got their P-40s up to 23,000 feet in order to be able to dive on the raiders, but they couldn't see anything. Then Holloway heard an excited voice over the radio: "Bandits! Twelve o'clock high!" Startled, he looked up. Not only were the Japanese bombers 3,000 feet above them, but there were many Zeros even higher. Apparently they hadn't seen the P-40s yet.

As he began a climbing turn, Holloway realized he was already too late to prevent some of the enemy bombers from hitting the field. He called to another group of P-40s to join the interception, and then began his own attack. Suddenly a Zero flashed in front of him. The Japanese bomber escort had decided to come to the rescue. Now the battle would be a tough one, fighter against fighter, but Holloway didn't hestitate.

Quickly he lined up the Zero in his sights and pressed the gun button. The P-40 shook from the recoil. The Zero broke up like a toy with a fire cracker in it, and Holloway's plane shot past it in a dive. He hauled his P-40 around and headed for the retreating bombers. Lining up one in his electric ring-sight, he waited until its wing filled the circle. Again his guns hurled a stream of lead at his victim, and again the target broke up under the terrific impact of the six .50-caliber machine guns.

Holloway looked around at the progress of the battle. He thought of conserving fuel in case he had to stay up to direct an interception against a second bombing attack. The air seemed strangely clear. Then he noticed a lone P-40 heading for a Zero that was trying to escape through the mountain valleys below. He couldn't resist the temptation to join in the hunt.

Thus began a dangerous chase through the hills at tree-top level. The throttles of all three fighters were wide open. Slowly the P-40s gained on the fleeing Zero, which could not turn either way because of the steep sides of the valley. If he tried

Chennault's pilots running to P-40s when they hear the air raid signal

to climb out, he would lose so much speed the Americans would be on him in a moment.

Then the Zero's luck ran out. The valley ended in a cliff and the Japanese pilot had to pull up. Holloway was on him immediately, and as his ring-sight filled with the Zero's silhouette he squeezed off a burst that caught the enemy fighter in the fuselage. The Zero stalled and, falling over on its back, hit the ground and exploded.

Holloway felt perspiration covering his hands and face. He was tense from the last hour of continuous fighting. Then came an urgent radio message from Kunming: "Second wave of enemy bombers headed toward field!"

Low on fuel and ammunition, Holloway nevertheless climbed to intercept the new threat while he called to the P-40 squadron at Changyi Field for help. Next he rounded up all the fighters who had taken part in the first attack and ordered them to head for nearby Yangkai Field so they wouldn't be caught on the ground while refueling.

He was dog-tired, but ready for what might come. Luckily the report of the second raid was false. The Japanese had had enough.

It had been an exceptional day, but there were many such days when the 23rd Fighter Group was in the air. On this occasion only one P-40 had been shot up, and it was landed safely by its pilot. Over fifteen Japanese fighters and bombers lay broken and burning in the hills of China and many more would not get back to their base.

By the end of the war Chennault's Fourteenth Air Force had destroyed 2,355 Japanese planes in the air and on the ground. Only 127 American planes were lost in aerial combat. It was a record unequaled in any other theater of war.

MESSERSCHMITT ME-109

4 Torch: The Desert Adventure

Late in 1942 an American carrier accompanied by four small escort carriers set a course out into the stormy Atlantic from Bermuda, which is almost a thousand miles off the eastern coast of the United States. They headed east but none of the fliers on board knew where they were going. They didn't know either that they were about to become part of the largest armada yet assembled.

When they were well at sea, Captain Calvin Durgin of the carrier *Ranger* called his Red and Blue Wildcat squadrons together and made an announcement:

"This is the start of the real second front of which there has been so much talk. . . ."

He told them they were on their way to take part in the invasion of North Africa. D-Day was to be November 8th. A giant force of 850 ships was on its way from England and America to join them. Part of the great fleet, along with the *Ranger,* would hit Casablanca, on the Atlantic coast of Africa in French Morocco. The rest of the armada would steam through the Strait of Gibraltar into the Mediterranean and strike Algeria.

Allied military might was not yet strong enough to attempt an invasion of Hitler's "Fortress Europe," but if the Allies could win control of North Africa they would be in an excellent position to strike at the "soft underbelly" of Europe. The veteran German Afrika Korps under General Erwin Rommel had driven the British back across the desert toward Egypt earlier in the year; but now British General Bernard Montgomery had rallied his Eighth Army. If Operation Torch—as the joint British-American invasion was called—proved to be a success, Rommel might be crushed between two powerful Allied forces.

Captain Durgin warned his *Ranger* fliers that they probably would be fighting Frenchmen at first instead of Germans, because Morocco was controlled by the pro-German elements of the French government. Of even more interest to the *Ranger's* fighter pilots was the fact that the French would be flying American planes bought from the United States many months before. Their squadrons included Curtiss P-36 "Hawks" and Douglas A-20 bombers, as well as their own Dewoitine 520 fighters. The American pilots were not to shoot first. But if the French wanted a fight the Americans were to give it to them. Captain Durgin told his pilots to call out, "Batter up!" if they were shot at. The carrier would signal back, "Play ball!" That would be the sign for everybody to attack.

On November 8th the "Red Ripper" squadron of F4Fs was up at 4:00 A.M. preparing for the

First army pursuit plane, P-40, to take off from the USS Chenango near Casablanca during the North African campaign

big day. At 7:00 the bull horn blasted through the *Ranger:* "Red squadron pilots man your planes!"

The Rippers, led by Lieutenant Commander Tom Booth, raced across the windy carrier to their Wildcats. One by one they roared down the flight deck and into the dawn. Their objective was Cazes airfield near Casablanca. As they neared Cazes, anti-aircraft fire reached up for the Red Rippers. The French were going to fight. Commander Booth called back to the *Ranger:*

"Batter up!"

Quickly the reply came: "Play ball."

"Here it is, boys," Tommy Booth said. "We're going in. Keep together."

They didn't stay together long. After the first strafing attack the Wildcat pilots found themselves split up. Lieutenant (jg) Charles August felt flak hit his F4F, but he thought the damage was slight. Suddenly he was attacked by French P-36s. He downed two of them and then found his own plane under fire. He was alone. The Curtiss Hawks were surprisingly maneuverable and he couldn't shake them. Luckily he spotted another Wildcat and recognized its pilot.

"Windy! . . . Windy, get those guys off my tail —quick!"

Windy Shields came diving to August's rescue.

F4F Wildcat fighters aboard the USS Santee preparing to take off at dawn for the North African invasion

Shields broke off the attack and shot down one P-36. Chuck August got the other. Shields had already destroyed one French fighter before he received August's call for help, and he was feeling good about his performance. But Shields and August did not stay together. Shields, alone, was attacked by more P-36s. He turned into them and shot down one but there were too many. He was trapped. He yelled into his mike: "This is Windy! Windy over Cazes! Attacked by four P-36s! Can't continue!" When the Wildcat caught fire, Shields bailed out. Chuck August had to hit the silk too.

Six Wildcats failed to return to the *Ranger* that day. The Red Rippers had destroyed a good many French planes, but they had made many mistakes. "They did not stick together," Tommy Booth said later. "The enemy fliers took advantage of it."

The American carrier pilots didn't make the same mistake again, and three days later the French surrendered.

But the main task lay ahead. Rommel's powerful desert army still had to be defeated.

Cochran's Red Scarf Guerrillas

On November 11th the first sizable flight of American fighter planes landed in North Africa. This was the 33rd Fighter Group flying P-40 "Warhawks." These P-40s were launched off the small aircraft carriers *Chenango* and *Archer* near Casablanca. The squadron leader of the thirty-five P-40s aboard the *Archer* was Major Phil Cochran, one of the most remarkable aerial commanders of the war. Some men are born leaders. Some are born fighter pilots. Phil Cochran was both. The 33rd had been sent to the Middle East, but there was little action there so Cochran brought his squadron back to Morocco for "further training." He was really looking for a fight.

The fight Cochran got was with his superiors. They dispersed his men, tried to take away his planes and ground him. Major Cochran had been itching for combat too long to accept such a situation. He climbed right back into his Warhawk and flew east alone. He was heading for Tunisia, where

Philip Cochran (Army Air Forces)

the Germans and Italians were slowly being trapped between converging Allied forces.

He landed at a small airfield near the front. He couldn't have picked a better spot. There was a P-40 squadron based on the field, but it was disorganized and morale was low. They were in poor condition to combat speedy German fighter planes like the Messerschmitt 109. Cochran took over.

Soon the squadron became the most effective aerial guerrilla unit in North Africa. They were known as the "Red Scarf Guerrillas." Not only did they meet the enemy in the air, they also harassed him on the ground. Cochran taught his pilots to destroy supplies, tanks, trucks and ammunition dumps. Some of his pilots, like Captain Levi Chase, showed an uncanny ability to spot enemy targets from the air. On one mission he destroyed eighty-four guns plus several trucks.

Chase is probably one of the few American

pilots given *credit* for destroying an American plane. One day he saw something strange on a road. It turned out to be the fuselage of an undamaged B-17 bomber which had made a forced landing in the desert and had then been captured by the Germans. Chase and his wingman strafed it and left it burning. Each received credit for one-half a Flying Fortress! Chase became known as Cochran's "One Man Wave of Terror."

The Red Scarf Guerrillas made their mark in the air too. Once they shot down more than thirty Axis planes in five days. They became so effective that the 12th Air Force finally assigned them some bombers. Major Phil Cochran had turned his disorganized P-40 squadron into a crack outfit. Later Cochran went to the China-Burma-India theater, where he continued his remarkable and ingenious leadership.

The Palm Sunday Massacre

As General Montgomery drove the Germans west from Egypt across Libya, he was helped immeasurably by the 57th American Fighter Group flying sturdy Warhawks. But the greatest day in the history of the Fighting 57th did not come until the Germans were bottled up in the northeastern tip of Tunisia. The Axis forces, surrounded on land and cut off by sea, could receive reinforcements and supplies only by air. Large convoys of lumbering tri-motored Junker 52s flew from enemy bases in Sicily to the African battle front. The American squadrons set up special fighter patrols to intercept this vital enemy life-line. On April 10th, for instance, a group of North American B-25 "Mitchell" light bombers and a P-38 escort attacked a fleet of gasoline-laden Junkers, sending twenty of them flaming into the Mediterranean.

What was needed, however, was a crushing blow that would make the Axis air lift too costly. It came a few days later on Palm Sunday.

Patrols had been out all day and found nothing. At five in the afternoon four squadrons of the 57th went out for the second time. They flew until they had only fifteen minutes' worth of fuel left. It looked as though the mission would be uneventful.

Then Captain Curl, the commander of the patrol, jerked upright in his seat. There to the right, coming in low over the sea were thirty . . . sixty . . . ninety Junkers! They had a fighter escort. Curl spoke into his mike: "Let's go get them, boys. Watch for the fighters."

The forty-seven Warhawks wheeled in a great diving turn and headed for the transports and their fighters. It was a massacre. The P-40s stayed

P-40 Warhawks taking off from their base in North Africa

in pairs and turned their full fury on the giant enemy formation. The battle lasted only ten minutes. As soon as a P-40 pilot destroyed one Junker he would line up another. Planes were falling into the Gulf of Tunis and crashing onto its shores in great burning arcs. The sky seemed filled with fire, and pillars of smoke rose from dozens of crashes.

The score was awesome: fifty-nine Junker transports had been destroyed, as well as sixteen Messerschmitt fighters. At least twenty more were probably destroyed or damaged. The 57th lost only six Warhawks.

Less than a month after this massacre the Germans were forced to surrender 270,000 troops to the victorious British-American armies in North Africa.

The battle across the deserts of North Africa,

like the fighting in the South Pacific, was a battle for airfields. The campaign lasted six months and during that time the Allies built over 350 airdromes. Leaders like Phil Cochran had shown that with control of the air one side could prevent the other even from moving.

Now that the Allies had the bases from which to launch an invasion of Sicily and Italy, American fighters and bombers swept up from North African bases to prepare the way. One of the most daring and successful fighter sweeps of the war was made during August, 1943, when 157 P-38 Lightnings attacked a group of enemy airfields at Foggia, Italy. The P-38s came across the Mediterranean, just skimming the water. As they neared Foggia they lowered their flaps so that the pilots had to point the noses of their fighters down to keep them from climbing. They came roaring over the airstrips at tree-top level with all guns blazing. A solid sheet of lead sprayed over the enemy bases like a deadly curtain. It was all over in ten seconds. Later, official Italian sources reported that 200 Axis planes had been destroyed or damaged.

American air power was on the march against the German conquerors. And far to the north, in England, Allied air bases were building up strength for future air battles that would be the greatest in history.

P-47 Thunderbolt

5 The Eagles Arrive

Immediately after the Japanese attack on Pearl Harbor, Germany and Italy declared war on the United States. Seventeen months later, on April 15, 1943, Don Blakeslee became the first American pilot in England to shoot down a German plane while flying an American fighter.

Our first bombers, B-17 Flying Fortresses, had arrived in England in July of 1942 to begin building up what was to be the greatest air armada in the world, the Eighth Air Force. But even before this, American fighter pilots had been fighting the Germans. These Americans were volunteers, and they flew English Hurricanes and Spitfires with the Royal Air Force.

They were called the Eagle Squadrons.

Don Blakeslee commanded one of these American squadrons. Blakeslee had been crazy about flying ever since he saw the Cleveland Air Races as a boy. He went to Canada for training with the Royal Canadian Air Force. Then early in 1941 he managed to get to England to take part in the fighting. Many other Americans were already there. Don Gentile was another Ohio boy who couldn't wait. He didn't have enough college credits to get into the United States Army Air Corps so he joined the RAF. Duane Beeson from Idaho—who would later become Gentile's chief scoring rival over Europe—had always wanted to be a lawyer. To earn his tuition he sold magazines and worked as a hotel clerk. But when war broke out, he entered the RAF and went on to become one of the deadliest shots in Europe. There were many others who wore the Eagle Squadron shoulder patch, including Jimmy Goodson, George Carpenter, Gus Daymond (who became the Eagle's high scorer) and Johnny Godfrey.

But certainly the most famous Eagle Squadron pilot was its first American commander, Chesley Peterson. Like many of his fellow Eagles, Peterson had tried to get into the United States Army Air Corps, but he was washed out for lack of "flying

Donald J. M. Blakeslee (Army Air Forces)

ability." Then when the determined young Peterson went to Canada to enlist, the neutrality laws stopped him. He tried again in June of 1940, and this time he succeeded. In England he learned to fly the Hawker Hurricane.

Chesley Peterson and the other Eagle Squadron members didn't get into the crucial Battle of Britain in which valiant English fighter pilots turned back the powerful German Luftwaffe. Soon, however, the Americans began to prove their usefulness. Peterson won the British Distinguished Flying Cross in October, 1941, and two months later the King personally awarded him the Distinguished Service Order.

One of the biggest days for the Eagles came on August 19, 1942, when they covered the commando raid on Dieppe, France, with two RAF squadrons. The Eagles flew three sorties over Dieppe that day. German opposition was determined and the battle became one of the most important fighter-plane duels of the war. As the swirling planes met in combat, the sky filled with smoke and flames. Blakeslee shot down two German fighters; Gentile flamed a fighter and then a bomber. Peterson was not so lucky. After destroying one German plane, he was hit himself and had to bail out over the English Channel. As he drifted down in his parachute, he amused himself by firing his pistol at the water, thinking he might not have another opportunity to shoot it. He was soon picked up by a rescue boat.

The following month the Eagles, like the Flying Tigers, were transferred into the American Air Forces. They became the nucleus of the 4th Fighter Group. As Eagles they had destroyed over seventy-three German aircraft. Of these the 71st Squadron, led by Peterson, accounted for forty-one. On the day they were transferred Sir W. Sholto Douglas, speaking for the British people, told them: "You joined us readily and of your own free will when our need was the greatest. There are those of your number who are not here today —those sons of the United States who were first to give their lives for their country. . . ."

The Famous "Jug"—the P-47

The new 4th Fighter Group liked just two things about belonging to the United States Army Air Forces—the higher pay and better food. They did not like the new plane they were given a few months later, the Republic P-47 "Thunderbolt." The Thunderbolt was a giant compared to the snappy little English Spitfire they had grown used to. The P-47 was a seven-ton monster with a 2,000 horsepower radial engine. It carried eight .50-caliber machine guns in its wings. The former Eagles thought the Thunderbolts looked like big milk bottles. They were disturbed when told that the plane wasn't supposed to fight below 18,000 feet. If it did it would lose its efficiency.

These feelings were natural after flying a small fighter like the beautiful Spitfire. In a climb it made the Thunderbolt look as if it were standing still. And the Spitfire could turn practically on a dime. The best German fighters, the Messerschmitt 109 and the Focke-Wulf 190, were good climbers too and highly maneuverable—and the Luftwaffe

P-47 Thunderbolt

British Spitfire

Captured German Messerschmitt

knew how to fight. The German fighter pilot received incredibly severe training. He was lashed to a revolving wheel and then asked to count the number of times he turned as well as do problems in arithmetic. He was shocked by electricity while cameras recorded his reactions. He was marched to a cliff and ordered to jump—if he hesitated he was washed out. If he passed these preliminary tests he was given rigorous flight training which amounted to a minimum of 300 hours in the air before entering combat.

In March, 1943, Peterson led the 4th Fighter Group on their first mission in the new Thunderbolts. The P-47s roared off from their base at Debden, England, and swept down the coast of France. They didn't see one German fighter. When they returned to Debden, Peterson confided, "I don't mind telling you I was scared."

The next month, Don Blakeslee scored the P-47's first kill. He dived on three Focke-Wulf 190s at 23,000 feet. His eight machine guns ripped into the German fighter, and Blakeslee followed it on down until it crashed. He was congratulated for proving that a Thunderbolt could outdive a FW-190.

"Heck, it ought to dive," Blakeslee said. "It certainly won't climb."

Enter the Wolf Pack

It was understandable why many of the former Eagles felt unhappy about the Thunderbolt, but a new American fighter group nicknamed the "Wolf Pack" was going to prove how wrong they were. The Wolf Pack had just arrived from the States, and its fliers began a rivalry with the 4th that lasted to the end of the war. Known officially as the 56th Fighter Group, it was commanded by one of the most remarkable combat leaders of the war,

Colonel Hubert "Hub" Zemke. Still in his twenties, he was an old hand with fighter planes. He had enlisted in the Army Air Corps in 1936, and for a while he was Phil Cochran's roommate at Selfridge Field. When Pearl Harbor was attacked, Zemke was in Russia demonstrating the P-40. He was called home to Mitchel Field to organize the 56th. None of the pilots Hub Zemke commanded had any previous combat experience except one, and he was a notable exception. Major Francis "Gabby" Gabreski had been stationed at Wheeler Field, Hawaii, on December 7, 1941. Immediately he asked to be assigned to a Polish-speaking squadron in the RAF so that he could gain valuable combat experience. He flew thirteen missions with them in Spitfires before he returned to the States to join Zemke's 56th as a squadron commander. Flying with the Wolf Pack, the colorful Gabreski was to become the leading fighter ace in the European Theater of Operations (ETO).

But if the group had no combat experience, they were eager to learn. And there was no better teacher than Zemke. Hub found another fine squadron commander in Major David Schilling. Then there were the two Johnsons (no relation)—Gerald W., who would become the group's first ace, and Bob, who would make twenty-eight air-to-air kills before his tour was over.

The pilots who trained with the 56th at Mitchel Field fell in love with the mammoth new P-47 Thunderbolt. They liked its rugged strength (it could take a terrific beating and still get its pilot home), and they learned how to take advantage of the fact that it could outdive any of the German planes. The heavy Thunderbolt was the first American fighter to fly into the sound barrier and not be destroyed. When pilots put the P-47 into a screaming dive from 35,000 feet it dropped like a bullet. The fliers also discovered the big P-47 could roll better than any other plane they had flown. This was a highly useful maneuver in combat.

Of course when the Wolf Pack got to England its pilots were warned that the Thunderbolt would be no match for the fast-climbing German planes. They were also told to watch out for yellow-nosed German fighter planes. Their pilots were the best in the Luftwaffe. Nevertheless, the pilots of the 56th Fighter Group were eager and ready to meet the Germans. They had confidence in Colonel Zemke and in their airplane.

On April 13, 1943, the Wolf Pack went into action on a Rodeo (a fighter sweep or patrol) over Calais, France. Nothing happened. Then on April 29th the 56th fought its first battle in the

Left to right: Hubert "Hub" Zemke, David C. Schilling and Robert S. Johnson (Army Air Forces)

skies over Europe. The Germans attacked head on and in pairs, cutting up the inexperienced American fliers. Two Thunderbolts were lost, together with their pilots, and three ships, including Dave Schilling's, were badly damaged. The Americans had hit no enemy planes.

Not until the middle of June did the Wolf Pack win its first victory. They had flown fighter sweeps and Ramrods (bomber escort), but the few times they ran into enemy fighters they came out the losers. They were getting anxious to even up things.

After one mission Schilling and Bob Johnson had been tongue-lashed by Zemke for leaving the formation to make a rash attack alone. That was a sure way to get killed. The very next day the eager Johnson again left formation in pursuit of a Focke-Wulf. He mistakenly thought a wingman was following him. As the FW-190 grew larger in his sight he squeezed his trigger. *Crash!* Johnson thought he had been hit but it was just the roar of his own guns. The Focke-Wulf exploded. Suddenly Johnson discovered he was alone. Luckily the fight had moved away from him or he would have been an easy victim himself. When he returned, Johnson was given another bawling out by his flight leader, but in general everybody in the 56th was feeling happy. Zemke had shot down two Focke-Wulfs and Gabreski had downed one too. The Wolf Pack was on its way.

On June 26th Bob Johnson learned just how much punishment the P-47 could take. The 56th was escorting a group of B-17s over an aircraft factory near Paris. Johnson swore he wouldn't leave the flight this time. Near Rouen he saw Focke-Wulfs rushing in from the rear. "Sixteen bandits, six o'clock, coming in fast!" he called over the radio. Nobody paid any attention. He called again. Johnson was frantic. He refused to leave the formation, but why didn't they turn to fight?

Suddenly he felt a shattering explosion. Then another. *Wham! Wham! Wham!* German cannon fire. His Thunderbolt shuddered and he lost control. Now bullets were peppering his plane. Then he smelled smoke! He yelled, "Mayday! Mayday!" —the call for help. Another explosion jarred the

P-47. Johnson tried to bail out but the canopy over the cockpit was stuck. The fighter, out of control, fell directly through the tight bomber formation, barely missing them.

Johnson fought the controls and finally pulled the Thunderbolt out of its spin. Oil spurted from the cowling and the engine was running so roughly he doubted he could get back to England. Then he was attacked again. A FW-190 made several passes at him and bullets riddled the P-47. The German pilot pulled up alongside the helpless fighter and saluted! Johnson thought he was letting him go. But no, the German was just saying good-by before shooting him down. Again machine guns raked the faltering Thunderbolt, with Johnson squeezing down behind his armor plate until the Focke-Wulf was out of ammunition.

Johnson finally made it back, but his plane would never fly again. It had been a bad day for the 56th; four pilots never returned at all. However, only two B-17s were hit by the sixty enemy planes attacking them. The fighters had protected the bombers.

On August 17th the 56th Fighter Group came back with a vengeance. In a Ramrod to Regensburg, Germany, Zemke led the Pack into a swirling aerial fight. Jerry Johnson destroyed three fighters and altogether the enemy lost at least seventeen planes.

A few days later the 56th shot down nine more German fighters.

And on August 24th Gabreski led his Avenger squadron in a daring attack which destroyed three Messerschmitts. In the last three missions the Wolf Pack had shot down twenty-nine planes while losing only four of their own.

The 4th Fighter Group wasn't doing quite so well. During their fighter sweeps, they rarely saw a German fighter, because the Germans were concentrating on Allied bombers. The bombers, of course, often flew so far that fighters could not escort them all the way to the target. Fighter Command worked out a partial answer: extra fuel tanks, streamlined like teardrops, were attached to the belly of the Thunderbolts. These could be dropped when the P-47s got into a fight.

The 4th tried out these drop-tanks for the first time in July. They were the first Allied fighters to penetrate beyond France and into Germany itself. As Peterson's Thunderbolts joined up with the Flying Fortresses over Germany, the big bombers were being cut up by almost sixty FW-190s, ME-109s and JU-88s. The P-47s roared to the bombers' defense and broke up the enemy attack. The Germans were astonished to see Allied fighters so far from England.

Francis E. Gabreski in a P-47 Thunderbolt with extra fuel tank attached below

On the sixteenth of August the 4th hit the Luftwaffe again—this time they were 20,000 feet above Paris. As the Thunderbolts took on the defending Germans, Don Blakeslee directed the complex battle from above—a new tactic devised by Fighter Command. Then he himself became involved in the spreading dogfight. Three FW-190s bounced him.

With alarm, Lieutenant James Goodson saw what was happening and called, "Break, Horseback Leader!" (Horseback was the code name for

German Focke-Wulf 190 in flight

the 4th Fighter Group.) Blakeslee pulled his P-47 into a steep vertical turn but the 190s hung on. Goodson closed in and his eight machine guns raked one of the attackers and then another. Both broke up in mid-air. But Blakeslee was hit too. Now Goodson crept up on the enemy fighter who was still shooting at Blakeslee. Suddenly Goodson's guns ran out of ammunition. Still he continued to fake his attack, and finally the Focke-Wulf was scared off.

Blakeslee in his crippled Thunderbolt, followed by Goodson and another P-47 pilot, headed for Debden. On the way back Goodson twice had to bluff off ME-109s who saw Blakeslee's damaged plane and thought he would be an easy mark.

The 4th Fighter Group set a new record for the ETO that day—eighteen German planes destroyed with only one loss to themselves. The new 56th group, however, was still pulling ahead in the total score column. In the five weeks before October the Wolf Pack shot down forty-three German planes, losing eight of their own. Then in October Zemke led his pilots on a rampage. Seven times the 56th met the Luftwaffe. Thirty-nine German fighters definitely never returned home, five more were probably destroyed, and eight were damaged. The remarkable thing was that the Pack lost only one of its own fighters. There were now five aces in the ETO, and four of them were from the Wolf Pack.

But Fighter Command still had a problem, and the fighter pilots knew what it was. On a mammoth bombing mission to Schweinfort on October 14th, *sixty* Flying Fortresses had been blown out of the sky by hundreds of attacking German fighters. Six hundred men were killed, wounded or captured on the tragic mission because the Thunderbolts and Lightnings could escort their big friends only halfway to their target. American fighter pilots knew they could beat the Germans now, but they needed longer legs.

In the meantime, on the other side of the world, the long struggle to win back the territory captured by the Japanese in the first months of the war was already under way.

P-38 LIGHTNING

6 The Long, Rough Road to Rabaul

The Pacific island was as strange and unknown as its name—Guadalcanal. It lay near the southern end of the Solomons, a chain of islands stretching into the Coral Sea just east of New Guinea. The Solomon Islands flanked Australia and were vital to its defense.

If you look at the map on pages 16–17 you will see another reason why Guadalcanal was important to the Allies. The Solomons, reaching up northwest from Guadalcanal in a double row, form a kind of channel between them called the "Slot." At the north end of the Slot is the island of Bougainville. And just after Bougainville comes New Britain, on which Rabaul is situated. At that time

Rabaul was the greatest Japanese stronghold in the whole southwest Pacific. So, in a sense, Guadalcanal could be the first step on a ladder which would lead us to Rabaul.

Aircraft carrier USS Wasp in flames off Guadalcanal

While United States forces were fighting in the Battle of the Coral Sea, the Japanese landed on Guadalcanal and began to build an airstrip. Hurriedly we drew up plans to crush them. On August 7, 1942, the First Marine Division invaded Guadalcanal. The landing itself was easy and the airstrip, renamed Henderson Field, was taken. But after that came months of the bloodiest, dirtiest fighting imaginable. Four major naval battles were fought in defense of the island, and time after time powerful Japanese convoys with reinforcements came down the Slot to wipe out the stubborn marines.

The Cactus Air Force

Almost the only outside help available to the marines came from the air. By August 20th, Henderson Field was completed and Marine Major John L. Smith flew in with nineteen Wildcats followed by twelve dive bombers. In the next few days some Army P-40s also landed and still later came torpedo planes and Navy fighters. Often all three services flew the same mission.

Day after day the Grumman Wildcats took off from dusty, muddy Henderson Field. They looked like stubby, blue-gray bumblebees as they swarmed into the sky to intercept large formations of Japanese bombers and fighters intent on destroying the

P-38 receiving repairs on an airfield at Guadalcanal

Marine base. The fliers called themselves the Cactus Air Force. On the ground they ate bad food and lived in dirty tents. At night, almost every night, they were bombed. And during the day, almost every day, they flew against the best and most experienced pilots Japan had.

Major Smith, a Medal of Honor winner, got his first Zero the day after he arrived. Before his tour of duty was over he had destroyed eighteen more, making him the first major American ace of World War II. Marion Carl, of Midway fame, wasn't far behind. On August 23rd, during the Battle of the Eastern Solomons, Carl flamed a Zero and two bombers. All in all the marines got sixteen planes that day, and lost only two of their own.

On August 30th, John Smith's F4Fs accounted for fourteen Japanese planes. Smith himself shot down four in a vicious fight, and Marion Carl got three. And so it went. When the Wildcats weren't fighting off attackers, they were escorting Marine bombers and torpedo planes over enemy targets. The relatively inexperienced Marine pilots had to learn fast. The Zero was a dangerous foe. Smith's men soon adopted the two-plane concept, developed by the Navy's Jimmy Thach, in which one Wildcat protected another. In this way the Cactus Air Force shot down five enemy planes for every one they lost in combat.

Early in October Major Duke Davis brought his 121st Fighter Squadron to the Canal to relieve Smith's heroic squadron, which had shot down 110 enemy planes. Davis' executive officer was a captain from South Dakota named Joseph Foss. On his first combat flight Foss shot down a Zero by chance—and was almost killed himself. He just managed to land his Wildcat deadstick (without power) at Henderson. But cigar-smoking Joe Foss was one who learned fast too. He was brave and an excellent marksman, already on his way to becoming the top ace in the Cactus Air Force.

But even with the new arrivals the heroic defenders could not cope with the overwhelming numbers of the enemy. In October Henderson

Marion E. Carl (Marine Corps)

Field came under heavy shelling from the Japanese fleet. It was left in a shambles; there were nineteen large craters in the runway alone. Most of our bombers were destroyed. Then the Japanese sent two convoys, protected by powerful ships, down the Slot. The planes that still were left at Henderson took off to stop the invasion, but they were too few. Thousands of fresh Japanese troops managed to get ashore.

Help was needed, desperately. Nineteen more Wildcats flew in led by Lieutenant Colonel "Indian Joe" Bauer. Bauer already had five Japanese planes to his credit. He had gotten them while voluntarily "visiting" Guadalcanal to see how things were coming along. Joe Bauer was considered by many who knew him to be the finest fighter pilot the Marines had. He proved it again the day he flew his squadron in to Henderson.

Just as his F4Fs were trying to land, the Japanese attacked the field with dive bombers. Bauer, his fuel almost gone from the trip up from Efate, tore into the bombers single-handed and shot down four of them. Those watching from below were awed by Indian Joe's courage and skill. When Bauer landed he called his pilots together. "Beginning tomorrow," he said, "things are going to be different. We have good planes and we can fly and shoot. We'll blast them out of the sky."

The next day he was as good as his word. At 15,000 feet he led his boys head on into a flight of twenty-one Zeros. Again Bauer got four himself in one spectacular dogfight, and his squadron got the rest. Marines in foxholes all over the island had seen the fight and stood up to cheer.

October was proving to be a full month for Joe Foss too. On the 18th Foss got three more kills (two of them Zeros), and he became an ace. Foss led a flight of eight Grumman Wildcats which he divided into the "Farm Boys" and the "City Slickers." Six of them became aces. On the 20th Foss got two more Zeros; on the 23rd four more; and on the 25th he shot down five Zeros.

On that impressive day Foss also witnessed a

close call by one of his fellow pilots, an impulsive scrappy lieutenant named Jack Conger. In a dog-fight low over the beach, Conger ran out of ammunition. Rather than let the Zero get away, Conger decided to ram him. His propeller chopped off the Zero's tail, but unfortunately Conger's F4F was damaged too and he had to bail out. As he hit the water, he saw the Japanese pilot parachute into the water just ahead of him. A rescue boat picked up Conger and then pulled up alongside the Zero pilot. Conger reached out to haul him in as a personal prisoner, but the Japanese pulled out a pistol. Aiming it at Conger's face, he squeezed the trigger. The gun failed to fire. Conger finally

Harold W. "Indian Joe" Bauer (left) and Joseph J. Foss (Marine Corps pilots)

Stanley W. Vejtasa (Navy)

James Flatley (Navy)

knocked him out with an oar.

Many of our pilots made it back to Henderson after being shot down in the jungle or at sea. Sometimes it took months, but with the help of friendly natives numerous Marine fliers who had been given up for dead suddenly stumbled back into camp. They were as good as ever after a few days' rest.

October was also the month of the Battle of Santa Cruz. On the 25th, the United States carriers *Hornet* and *Enterprise* met a superior enemy naval force northeast of Guadalcanal and stopped it from supporting the Japanese on the island. Commander Jimmy Flatley's fighter group, the Grim Reapers, formed after the Battle of the Coral Sea, made a good accounting of themselves in this fight. Unfortunately John Leppla, who had done so well in that earlier battle, was shot down by two Zeros. But Swede Vejtasa tried to make up for the loss of his friend. From 13,000 feet he screamed down at eleven torpedo bombers heading for his fleet. At 400 miles an hour he closed on the attackers and one by one he began cutting them down. Four fell smoking into the Pacific. Vejtasa flashed by, turned and began hunting the rest of the scattered bombers. Relentlessly he caught three more. When he ran out of ammunition he at least had the satisfaction of knowing he had destroyed a record seven enemy planes in one engagement.

On November 11th the Japanese made a final, do-or-die push on the battered island. They sent eleven transports, heavily supported by almost one hundred ships. Enemy cruisers shelled Henderson Field. American bombers headed for the transports coming down the Slot, while the Wildcats, P-40s and P-39s beat off strong attacks from the air. Joe Foss led off the fighters on the twelfth of November, and together they downed seventeen bombers and six Zeros. Our dive and torpedo bombers were magnificent too. Every plane that could fly hit the transports. Seven were sunk and the rest badly damaged. Over 6,000 Japanese troops were lost along with their supplies. It was the greatest victory Marine aviators had in World War II.

To accomplish the feat, help had been flown in from everywhere. Among the special recruits was Jimmy Flatley, who had brought his Reapers in to Henderson Field from the *Enterprise.* As soon as he landed he ran over to his old friend Joe Bauer, who was sitting in a warmed-up Wildcat.

"Where you going, Joe?" Flatley yelled.

"I'm going up to see for myself what the convoy looks like," Bauer told him. As fighter commander of the Cactus Air Force, he didn't get to fly as much as he liked.

On his way back to Henderson after viewing the carnage, Bauer was jumped by several Zeros. He shot down one but the control cables on his Wildcat had been cut during the flight. Joe Foss saw Bauer hit the water and then begin swimming. Foss headed back for Henderson full throttle. He made a hot landing and ran to operations.

"The Japs got Joe!" he cried.

Some volunteers went out to search for Colonel Bauer but he was never found. For weeks after that the pilots sat around at night and told stories about the heroic exploits of Indian Joe Bauer—and they probably tell them still.

The Japanese were forced to give up Guadalcanal. Bitter fighting continued until February 7, 1943, but there was no longer much doubt about the outcome. Many fighter pilots were given leave for a while in Sydney, Australia, and then returned before the finish. Joe Foss was one of these. On January 15th, Foss knocked down three more Zeros to bring his score to twenty-six. He was the first American to equal Captain Eddie Rickenbacker's World War I record (and four of Rickenbacker's victories had been balloons). As a fighter pilot and as a leader he was unexcelled. Joe Foss was quick to give credit to his men, and they in turn had no doubt that he was the best.

The Death of Yamamoto

Now the Americans were ready to crack another link in the Solomon chain. This was the Japanese-held island of New Georgia, one step closer to Rabaul. The Marines again were the spearhead.

But Admiral Yamamoto did not take the loss of Guadalcanal lightly. He came down to Rabaul personally to take charge. He ordered all-out attacks to be made on New Guinea and the Guadalcanal area. The first blow came on April 1st. Fifty-eight Zeros swarmed over Guadalcanal. They shot down six of our planes, but lost eighteen of their own fighters doing it.

Then on April 16th, Yamamoto sent 67 Val dive bombers and 110 Zeros down to the Solomons. We had only seventy-six Marine, Navy and Army fighters to oppose them. But that day we

James E. Swett
(Marine Corps)

shot down thirty-eight Japanese planes, and lost only one American pilot.

The most remarkable performance of the day was given by a young Marine fighter pilot who had never been in combat before. He was a 22-year-old lieutenant named James "Zeke" Swett, and he led a four-plane division of Wildcats. From 15,000 feet he pushed his F4F over and headed for the Vals. Like a veteran, Swett hung on the tails of the diving bombers and sent three of them crashing into Tulagi below. As he was pouring slugs into the third bomber, his Wildcat was accidentally hit in the wing by friendly anti-aircraft fire from below. He pulled out of the fight for an instant to check the damage, saw it was not too bad and headed immediately for five more Vals he spotted trying to slip away. He closed in on the bombers, one by one, and shot them down—all except the last one.

The Val had a machine gun facing aft and this time the rear-gunner was ready. Bullets smashed into Swett's cockpit, sending flying glass into his face. His engine was also hit. But the Marine pilot continued to return the fire, and the last he saw of the bomber it was smoking. He crash-landed safely in the water after again being shot at by American ground fire. In fifteen minutes he had destroyed seven enemy planes and a possible eighth. Jimmy Swett was another marine who well deserved the Medal of Honor he was awarded.

Yamamoto's grandiose plan for revenge was a flop, but he was never to know it. He decided to make an inspection trip to Kahili airfield on Bougainville, the northernmost island in the Solomons and his biggest base south of Rabaul. The Americans knew about Yamamoto's trip because the Japanese secret code had been broken.

Admiral Marc Mitscher called in his Fighter Commander, Lieutenant L. S. Moore. "Sam," he said, "work me up a plan to get this bird."

With the help of the Army a plan was devised. The P-38 was the only fighter that could do the job, for the round trip from Guadalcanal to Kahili was over 1,000 miles. Army Major John Mitchell's squadron was given the honor. Mitchell himself would fly top cover with twelve P-38s while his "trigger section"—his best shots—attacked Yamamoto's plane just before it landed.

The timing of the P-38s was perfect. They reached Kahili just as the Japanese Admiral's plane, with its protective Zero cover, circled to land. There were four "shooters," but only two got in on the kill. One of the others couldn't eject his belly tank, and his wingman had to stay with him for protection. Captain Thomas Lamphier dived his Lightning toward Yamamoto's plane. A Zero got in the way and Lamphier shot it down. Then he lined up the Admiral's bomber in his sights and let his .50-caliber guns roar. They sawed off the bomber's wing, and Yamamoto went to a swift death in the jungle below. Lamphier's wingman, Lieutenant Rex Barber, attacked and shot down the bomber accompanying Yamamoto's. It carried his chief of staff.

Overhead Mitchell's fighters held off the frantic Zeros and even shot down three. Only one Army pilot was lost.

Japan's greatest military mind was gone, and the most daring interceptor raid of the war was an unqualified success. For weeks afterward P-38s flew patrols near the area so the Japanese would think the first flight had been there only in the normal line of duty. We did not want the Japanese to know we had broken their code.

Pappy and His "Black Sheep"

There was a new fighter plane in the Pacific. One writer said it looked like "a blue ballbat with inverted gull wings." It was the Chance-Vought F4U "Corsair," and it was just what the Marine fliers wanted. The Corsair was the first American fighter plane that was better than the Japanese Zero in almost every way. It could climb higher and faster (nearly 3,000 feet a minute), and it could fly twice as far as the Wildcat. Many Japanese pilots thought it was the finest American fighter they encountered. They named it "The Whistling Death" because of the frightening sound it made in a dive.

Lieutenant Kenneth Walsh was one of the first Marine fliers to rack up a big score with the F4U. He had over 2,000 hours in the air and had been with the Marines ten years. Though he had had three planes shot from underneath him, he always came back for more. Once after destroying three enemy planes over Vella Lavella he landed safely at Munda in a Corsair which was so badly shot up that it had to be junked immediately. Another time he single-handedly engaged almost fifty Japanese planes over Kahili and knocked down four of them. Before he left the Solomons he had twenty victories to his credit. For his extraordinary heroism he too received the Medal of Honor.

New Georgia finally fell, and next we went after Kahili and the other airfields on Bougainville. We knew that the Japanese would try to defend Kahili with everything they had; after all it was their chief base in the Solomons. The Army, Navy and Marines all sent fighters and bombers for the attack. We intended to invade Bougainville on November 1st, but its defenses had to be destroyed first.

There was one Marine pilot in particular who came up with his own way to knock down the Japanese aerial defenses. His name was Gregory Boyington, formerly one of Chennault's Flying Tigers. Boyington thought the answer to the problem of enemy aerial defense was the "fighter sweep." By this he meant that fighters should be sent out to hunt down enemy planes—and not used just to protect an airfield or to escort bombers.

Major Boyington's story was an unusual one. When he left the Flying Tigers, he had a hard time getting back into the Marines. And after he got back in he was not assigned to combat. Finally he asked permission to form his own fighter squadron out of a replacement pool of pilots. He trained them in record time in his own hard, aggressive way. His men began to call him Pappy —he was older than they were—and they called

Boyington outlining flight instructions to his men

themselves the Black Sheep.

Pappy's first combat as a marine came on September 16, 1943. The Black Sheep were to escort 150 Avengers and Dauntlesses on a strike aimed at Bougainville. Boyington once described a fighter pilot's mission as "hours and hours of dull monotony sprinkled with a few moments of stark horror." The horror came soon enough, but most of it was suffered by the Japanese. Pappy was so tense on his first contact with the defending Zeros that he forgot to turn on his gun switches. He quickly got hold of himself, however, and sent a Zero down in flames. The second one he hit exploded right in front of him; he was so close he had to fly through the debris. He got three more before heading for home that day. When he landed, his engine cut out on the taxi way from lack of fuel. His armorers found he had only thirty rounds of .50-caliber left.

But Pappy didn't like escorting bombers. He wanted to be free to attack when and where he wished. One day the bombers which the Black Sheep were to protect didn't show up. Boyington decided to stay over Kahili anyway for some action. Suddenly Pappy got a call on his radio. It was from a Japanese pilot pretending he was an American, and Pappy knew it.

"Major Boyington, what is your position?"

Pappy told him. He also said he was at an altitude of 20,000 feet when he was really at 25,000.

The next thing the Black Sheep saw was a formation of thirty Zeros rendezvousing 5,000 feet beneath them. The whole squadron of Corsairs pushed over and screamed toward the unsuspecting Japanese. The Zeros tried to scatter but were trapped. Pappy got three of them himself—in just thirty seconds! The fighter sweep was beginning to pay off and the enemy knew it.

The next time the Black Sheep flew over Kahili the Japanese stayed on the ground. Pappy taunted them by radio: "We're right over your airport. Why don't you come up and fight?" He called them names. There were no takers.

But Pappy constantly thought of ways to lure the Zeros into the air. Once the Black Sheep flew over very high in a big V formation as if they were dive bombers. The Zeros were fooled and took off to intercept. That day the Japanese lost ten more planes for good, three of them personally shot down by Boyington.

Kahili and its nearby base were pounded into dust by daily raids. The air was so clear of Zeros

P-39s ready for take-off at Bougainville

Gregory "Pappy" Boyington (Marines)

that the Dauntless and Avenger pilots grew bored with the routine. The invasion of Bougainville was a success.

Ring Around Rabaul

American forces were at the gates of the Japanese stronghold—Rabaul itself. Japan had lost over 2,000 planes so far in the battle for the Solomons, and the Marine fliers had accounted for three-fifths of them. Rabaul was now about to fall under heavy attack from all three services: the Army, Navy and Marines.

The P-38 Lightnings of General Kenney's Fifth Air Force were well on their way to shooting down more Japanese planes than any other American fighter.

By the end of July, 1943, Kenney's "bad boy," Dick Bong, had sixteen victories, as did Tommy Lynch.

In September another outstanding fighter pilot came to Kenney's attention. He was Lieutenant Colonel Neel Kearby, who flew a fighter plane new to the Pacific area, the P-47 Thunderbolt. Neel Kearby knew he could beat anybody with it, and by the end of the month he had destroyed eight Japanese planes. He was catching up to Bong, whose P-38 had been so badly shot up he

Richard I. Bong (Army Air Forces)

was grounded until he could get another.

On October 11th Kearby really went to work. On a sweep over New Guinea with his "Three Musketeers" he shot down an enemy plane. Immediately afterward he sighted a formation of thirty-three bombers and twelve Zeros. Kearby signaled for an attack. Working his way through the formation he flamed three; then he came back and destroyed two more which were after his wingmen. He practically ripped another Zero in two with his guns, but his gun camera ran out of film and he was never given credit for the seventh victory.

Six victories in one combat was a record at that time, and for the feat Neel Kearby received the

Medal of Honor. His total now was fourteen, only three short of Bong. Bong didn't let up, however. On two successive raids over Rabaul he downed four more planes, bringing his record up to twenty-one. Kenney thought it was time to send him back to Poplar, Wisconsin, for a well-earned rest.

By the time Dick Bong returned to the South Pacific in February, Kearby had upped his score to twenty, and Tommy Lynch claimed eighteen victories. Then both Bong and Lynch were assigned to the staff of the Fifth Fighter Command. They were told to stay out of combat. Orders were orders, of course, but neither pilot liked the idea of a desk job and somehow each managed to fly a combat patrol fairly often. Shortly after Bong's return, Neel Kearby shot down two Zeros. But on the same day Bong got one himself, so now the score was tied at twenty-two.

Kearby was determined to break the tie. On March 4th he went out looking for trouble, and found it. He attacked a Japanese formation of fifteen planes and claimed two of them. But Neel Kearby's number was up. A Zero dived on him and sent his Lightning plunging into the jungle. On March 9th Tommy Lynch was killed, too. Dick Bong saw him fall.

A race was also developing among Marine

Robert M. Hanson (Marines)

Neel E., Kearby (Army Air Forces)

fighter pilots. The concept of the fighter sweep was being used against Rabaul. Pappy Boyington fittingly led the first sweep—nearly 100 fighter planes of all types—but he soon discovered this was too many planes. He felt he could do better with half that number. On December 23rd he proved his point. With forty-eight fighters he caught forty Zeros completely off guard. Thirty Zeros fell in flames. The Black Sheep accounted for twelve of them and Pappy himself got four. His score was now twenty-four victories, only two away from Joe Foss's record.

Boyington got another Zero on December 27th, but he was disgusted with his performance. He thought his score should have been higher. His tour was just about up and he was getting record-conscious.

On the day of his last mission he was so tense he could hardly talk to anyone. He took off and led his flight toward Rabaul. War correspondents and friends waited anxiously at his field for his return. Pappy didn't come back. One of the pilots in his sweep reported seeing Boyington shoot down a Zero, so at least he had equaled Foss's mark. Nothing more was known until after the war when Pappy emerged from a Japanese prison camp. He'd been shot down finally, and almost drowned too, but before his Corsair fell he'd destroyed two more Zeros, bringing his score to twenty-eight. Pappy Boyington became the Marines' top ace.

Boyington could not be replaced, but there were plenty of Army, Navy and Marine pilots to carry the fight to Rabaul. One other marine stood out in particular. He was Lieutenant Robert Hanson. His record was so remarkable that he won the nickname "Butcher Bob." He had five victories over Bougainville before he came up to Rabaul. There, beginning on January 14, 1944, he set a pace no one else in the whole war ever equaled. On his first sortie he shot down five more Zeros. The next time he went up he got another. On his third flight he added three more. He got four the following trip. Then he knocked down three on his fifth mission, and on his sixth he flamed four again. In the amazingly short span of seventeen days he had accounted for twenty Zeros, bringing his grand total to twenty-five.

Hanson's was an almost unbelievable accomplishment, and it happened so quickly that few knew about it at the time. Ironically he was killed on a strafing run by ground fire shortly afterward. He was to have been sent home in a week.

Rabaul became the perfect hunting ground for fighter pilots. For instance, Captain Donald Aldrich shot down twenty planes, and Captain Harold Spears got fifteen. The Japanese could not stand that kind of fighting. Thousands of sorties were flown against the base, and slowly it lost its strength to hit back. By March the air power at Rabaul had collapsed.

It was decided that instead of invading Rabaul, which still had dangerous shore batteries, we would simply by-pass it. We continued to raid the base until the end of the war to keep it neutralized. But it would no longer be a threat to anyone.

American aviators had seen to that.

FOCKE-WULF FW-190

7 "Achtung, Indianers!"

Lieutenant John Godfrey was typical of the fighter pilots in the 4th Fighter Group who had once been members of the Eagle Squadrons in England. He was aggressive and adventurous and had come to war earlier than most other Americans by enlisting in the Royal Canadian Air Force. He also loved the trim and nimble Spitfire and at first didn't care much for the Thunderbolt when he transferred to the Army Air Forces.

Other fliers generally agreed that Godfrey had the sharpest eyes in the 8th Air Force. He shot down his first plane in November, 1943, when he dived out of formation on a Messerschmitt 109 which no one else saw. The 109 exploded and

Godfrey's P-47 flew right through the debris. "Then a strange exhilaration mixed with a horrible feeling of remorse overcame me," he wrote later. "I'd destroyed my first plane, and undoubtedly killed a man—I trusted that God would understand."

When he returned to Debden, Don Blakeslee bawled him out for breaking formation; but, like Bob Johnson in the 56th, Godfrey was tired of waiting for the Germans to come up to the extreme altitude at which the Thunderbolts flew. He wanted to fight. He was also depressed about the record the 56th, a comparatively new group, was making. The 56th had now destroyed over 200 enemy planes, while the score of the 4th Fighter Group was only 170.

And it seemed as if the 56th was just getting warmed up. On November 26th, Lieutenant Colonel David Schilling, Zemke's executive officer, led the fighter group out to protect 633 bombers returning from a mission to Bremen. The Germans attacked the bombers in force. Most of the enemy planes were twin-engined Messerschmitt 110s armed with rockets. The American pilots called them "meat on the table," because they were easier to shoot down than the speedier and more dangerous 109s and Focke-Wulfs. With Schilling in the lead the Thunderbolts dropped out of the

Pilots of the famed 56th Fighter Group. Standing, from left: Francis Gabreski, Robert Johnson, Walker Mahurin, Robert Landry; seated, Walter Cook and David Schilling

sun on the Messerschmitts. Schilling and Jerry Johnson got two, as did Gabreski, who was now an ace. The star of the day, however, was Major Walker "Bud" Mahurin, who downed three 110s to bring his total score to eleven. Altogether the 56th knocked down twenty-three enemy fighters and lost none themselves.

Actually Bud Mahurin had destroyed another plane—a bomber—but it was never entered in the official records because it was American. Mahurin was an exuberant flier and one day he began a mock battle with a Consolidated B-24

"Liberator" over England. On one of his practice passes he came so close that the Liberator's propellers cut off the tail of his P-47 and he had to bail out. The Liberator crash-landed.

On December 11th, the Wolf Pack ran wild again.

The Ramrod began as a routine escort mission. Two hundred fighters were to escort five hundred heavy bombers—B-17s and B-24s—on their way to blast Emden, Germany. The 56th was only part of this formation, of course, but it was an important part.

Francis Gabreski was leading his "Avengers" high above the first formation of bombers when he sighted more than forty single-engine German fighters and sixty Messerschmitt 110s getting ready to fire their deadly rockets into the "flying box" of bombers. Gabby never used tracer bullets in his guns. "Sometimes you miss with the first shots," he said, "and the tracers give you away." As Gabreski turned his squadron to attack, the two P-47s directly over him collided with a shattering explosion. The blast lit up the sky and the Germans suddenly saw the Avengers. "*Achtung, Indianers!*" they called urgently to one another. It meant, "Look out, Indians!"—meaning Americans.

The enemy fighters tried to scatter. Gabreski ordered an attack and the fourteen Avengers plunged toward the enemy. Soon there was no pattern to the fight. Planes zoomed and dived, guns blazing continually. The fighting seemed to go on for hours, though really it was only a matter of minutes. When the deadly contest was over, three of the Avengers had scored three kills apiece, two more had two apiece and Bob Johnson got his Number Seven. Gabreski blasted a ME-110 but then found himself alone. He was almost out of fuel, so he headed for home using as little power as possible.

Suddenly a single plane came toward him. It was an ME-109! Gabreski turned into the enemy to try to scare him off, but soon the German pilot realized that his victim was not able to fight with full combat power because he was low on gasoline. The Messerschmitt made several passes at the Thunderbolt. Just as Gabreski was pulling up into a sharp zoom, he felt cannon shells smashing into his plane. He put his Thunderbolt into a spin and stayed in it until he had fallen at least 10,000 feet. There was a cloud bank just ahead and Gabreski suddenly stopped the spin and raced for it. The Messerschmitt pilot saw the trick—but too late. Gabby roared into the cloud and safety. He just made it to his field before his tanks went dry.

On this mission only 17 of the 500 bombers

were knocked down, thanks to aggressive fighter defense; and the Wolf Pack moved still further ahead in the scoring column.

As if they weren't doing well enough, the Wolf Pack received a present on New Year's Day, 1944, aimed at increasing their record performance. Republic engineers had invented a new broad-bladed propeller for the Thunderbolt which made it climb like a scared cat. It could even out-perform the Spitfire now.

The Blakesleewaffe

At the same time important things were happening in the 4th Fighter Group. Colonel Chesley Peterson was replaced by Colonel Don Blakeslee as commander of the 4th. Colonel Peterson had flown countless hours of combat by now, and the Old Eagle was suffering combat fatigue, as did most pilots who had flown as long as he had. Blakeslee too had flown hundreds of missions by this time, but Colonel Don—as his pilots called him—seemed to be an iron man. The more he flew the stronger he got. No other flier at Debden had his stamina. He thought of deadly aerial combat as "a grand sport." Blakeslee, of course, loved to fly; but he wasn't a good shot. Even at that he became a double ace, though he never painted swastikas on his plane to chalk up his kills. He flew more combat missions—over 500—and logged more combat hours than any other American in the war. Not all of his men loved him, but every one thought he was the best leader in the world.

Then late in 1943 a fresh group of fighter pilots from the Ninth Air Force (formerly in North Africa) arrived in England. Known as the "Pioneer Group," they were flying a new airplane—the North American P-51 "Mustang." Blakeslee was assigned to lead the inexperienced Pioneers on their first few missions.

The Pioneers were quick to learn, and their new plane gave them confidence. Moreover there were several veterans in the 9th. One of the most outstanding was Major James Howard, a former Flying Tiger. On January 11th, Major Howard led his fighters on an escort mission over Germany. Enemy fighter planes attacked the bombers, and almost immediately Howard found himself alone. The fight had broken up his group. He saw that the bombers were still under heavy fire from the Germans. Rather than wait to reassemble his pilots he unhesitatingly headed his lone fighter into a formation of more than thirty Messerschmitts and Focke-Wulfs. For thirty minutes he not only held off the swarming enemy but also shot down three German fighter planes and damaged six more.

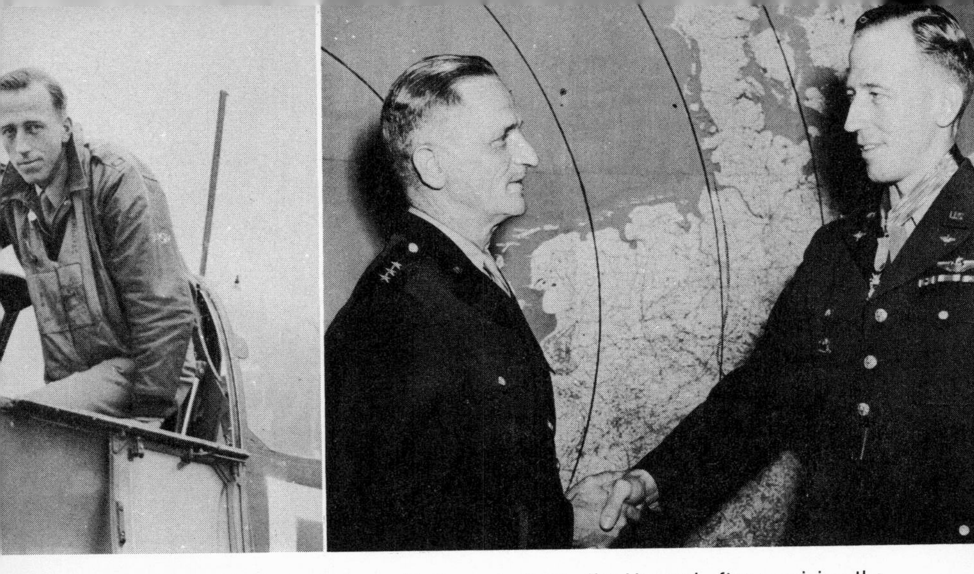

James H. Howard (Army Air Forces). Right: Jim Howard after receiving the Congressional Medal of Honor from General Carl A. Spaatz.

The bomber crews were loud in their praise of Major Howard when they returned. Their reports were so enthusiastic that Jim Howard was awarded the Congressional Medal of Honor and promoted to lieutenant colonel.

When Blakeslee came back to the 4th all he could talk about was the new fighter plane. The Mustang could outclimb, outdive, outturn, outspeed any other fighter plane around. More than that it had the range to follow the bombers all the way to the target and back. It was like the Spitfire that the ex-Eagles remembered so fondly, but it was even better.

Colonel Don wanted the Mustang for the 4th. He went personally to Major General William Kepner, Fighter Command Chief of the Eighth Air Force. Kepner told him that all the Mustangs were going to the Ninth Air Force pilots, who were preparing for the invasion of Europe. Besides, he pointed out, it would take too long to train the 4th to fly the new fighter. Mustang pilots usually had 200 hours of practice in them before entering combat.

"General," Blakeslee said, "give me those Mustangs and I give you my word—I'll have 'em in combat in twenty-four hours. I promise—twenty-four hours."

General Kepner finally agreed.

And so it was that in late February, 1944, Blakeslee's 4th Fighter Group got the plane they had been waiting for. "You can learn to fly 'em on the way to the target," Blakeslee told them—and that's just what they did.

There were now more than 1,000 American fighter planes in the Eighth Air Force and over 2,000 bombers. The Germans were stronger than ever too. The coming months—March and April—would mark the Great Days of the famous air battles over Europe.

The Big "B"

Early in the war, Reichsmarshal Hermann Goering, chief of the Luftwaffe, promised Hitler that Berlin would never be bombed. On March 4,

1944, he received the shock of his life. Not only did a few American Flying Fortresses appear over Germany's capital city, but they were escorted by scarlet-nosed Mustangs. "When they came with fighter escort over Berlin," Goering said, "I knew the jig was up."

Don Blakeslee was in that first P-51 over Berlin. It was a long flight and most of the bombers didn't make it because of bad weather. Many Mustangs had to turn back too because the new plane was still plagued by minor mechanical difficulties. (Blakeslee's guns jammed but he continued on anyway.) By the time they got to Berlin there were only eight P-51s left. They ran into sixty German fighters and fought their way out.

But they would be back.

Two days later, on March 6th, a gigantic aerial force crossed the English Channel headed for the heart of Germany. Over one thousand Liberators and Flying Fortresses stretched fifteen miles across the sky. They carried three thousand tons of high explosive, nineteen million rounds of machine-gun ammunition, and over three million gallons of gasoline. They droned on almost five miles above the earth, and were surrounded by hundreds and hundreds of Eighth Air Force fighters.

Colonel Blakeslee's group led the first large formation of bombers over Berlin, while back along

"Flak Highway" other fighter groups, including the 56th, fought off German attacks. The Germans threw every available plane at the bombers. Overhead Blakeslee directed the complex battle as only he could:

"Shirtblue Red Section, break up that gaggle of 110s coming in on that Fort at four o'clock. . . . Red Three, give that 109 some more—he's not burning yet. . . . Greenbelt squadron, don't point your dumb noses at those bombers"—the Fortresses would shoot at anything that looked as if it were attacking them—"Those two Mustangs under the first box of bombers—form up on me. . . ."

Blakeslee himself shot down an enemy fighter, and the rest of his group was having a field day.

Farther back Zemke's Wolf Pack was doing better than usual too. Bob Johnson's squadron of eight Thunderbolts took on more than 150 German fighters and broke them up. Johnson, raging with anger every time he saw a B-17 hit, roared after two Messerschmitts which had just scored on a lumbering Fortress. He hit the leader; then he exploded another enemy plane which was closing in on a P-47. Zemke himself got three kills that day. A great many bombers—too many—never returned to England, but the Germans had been met and fought all the way to the target. The Luftwaffe had lost a great many fighters and—

more important—irreplaceable pilots.

Obviously German flak and fighter opposition was still dangerously strong, but the Eighth Air Force was not going to stop now. Just two days later another "maximum effort" was mounted. As the battle started high over Berlin, a new fighter team was born. General "Hap" Arnold was to call it "the greatest of any war." John Godfrey had finally found a leader he was willing to follow without question, and Don Gentile had found a wingman he could trust completely.

Godfrey had flown on Gentile's wing the first fight he was ever in. Today, by chance, the two were together again. Gentile was a quiet, handsome boy who puzzled the fun-loving extroverts at Debden; in the air, however, he became the bold hunter. Don Gentile was out to beat them all, but the other pilots didn't know it. Godfrey was about to be the first to understand the real skill Gentile possessed.

When they reached the bombers on the outskirts of Berlin, the German fighters were already attacking. Godfrey and Gentile closed in on five Messerschmitt 109s. After several tight turns Godfrey got onto the tail of one.

"I've got you covered!" Gentile yelled.

Godfrey saw his bullets striking the 109.

Gentile, the more experienced, was coaching

him: "Give him more . . . more!" Godfrey continued to fire until the German pilot bailed out.

Then Gentile zoomed to within seventy-five yards of another 109 and shot it down. Immediately he saw another one.

"Johnny, cover me. I'm diving on the Jerry at three o'clock."

"Right behind you, Don."

Gentile, safe in the knowledge that he couldn't be attacked from the rear, concentrated on the 109 ahead and blasted him out of the sky. By now the two pilots were in the middle of a gigantic fight. Gentile saw two more 109s directly ahead.

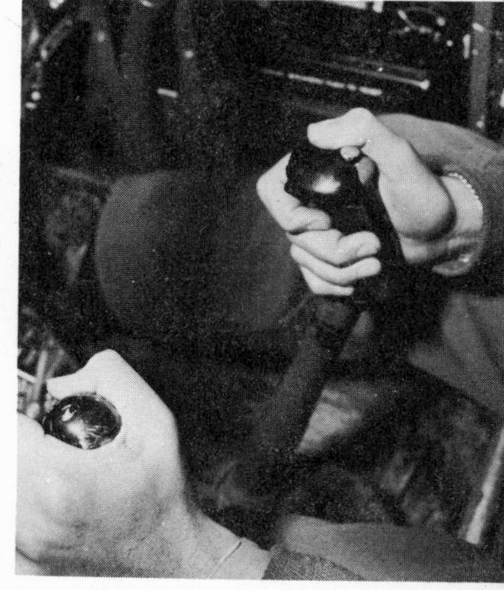

Don S. Gentile (Army Air Forces). Right: Close-up of Gentile's trigger finger technique for firing on Nazi aircraft.

"All right, Johnny," Gentile radioed, "you take the one on the right and I'll get the other."

Another Mustang pilot tried to follow Gentile and Godfrey as they headed for the Germans. He had seen what success they were having and hoped to be a part of it. Both Gentile and Godfrey began firing at the same time. Ahead of them the two Messerschmitts burst into flame and fell off toward earth. The Mustang pilot who was trying to keep pace with the remarkable team gave up. He had never seen two fighters work so well together. Their combined score was now five.

As they climbed back to 22,000 feet Godfrey spotted another 109 making a head-on attack at them.

"All right," Gentile said, "when I give the order, you break right and I'll break left."

Suddenly Gentile yelled, "Now!"

Both pilots hauled back on their sticks and came down in an arc on the Messerschmitt's tail. The German went into a steep dive but could not shake the Mustangs.

"You take him, Don," Godfrey called. "I'm out of ammo."

Gentile finished off the job. At less than 1,000 feet the German pilot hit the silk.

But the boys in the 56th weren't idle either. Bud Mahurin flamed three German fighters. This

Robert Johnson (left), Walker M. "Bud" Mahurin (right) and an unidentified crew member

made him the leading scorer in the ETO with twenty-one kills. And Bob Johnson wasn't far behind with eighteen. A week later Johnson passed Mahurin's record. He was leading a squadron of eight Thunderbolts on a Ramrod when he ran into a large formation of Focke-Wulfs at 27,000 feet. Johnson led his planes directly into the Germans and broke them up. Then he saw fifty more Focke-Wulfs roaring down on him from 35,000 feet!

Johnson yelled to his squadron, "Okay, pull straight up—*now!* The top cover's coming down." Eight P-47s suddenly zoomed into vertical climbs, all guns firing. The Germans were taken by surprise and broke frantically to avoid the flying wedge made by the Thunderbolts.

Johnson now called for help. Thunderbolts and Lightnings came from all directions. Soon there was a mad, swirling dogfight involving at least 300 fighters. It ranged from 30,000 feet right down to the ground. The 56th Fighter Group knocked down twenty-four German planes and not one enemy fighter got through to the bombers. Johnson himself shot down three Focke-Wulfs.

Aggressive American fighter groups had the Germans on the run. The spirit of competition ran high. On the same day Bob Johnson got his twenty-first victory, Lieutenant Ralph "Kid" Hofer of Blakeslee's group shot down two FW-109s near Munich, Germany. Then he lost his squadron and his radio went out. As if that weren't enough, the device which governed his propeller pitch went out of control and the propeller wouldn't pull any more. He headed over the Alps into Switzerland, where he could bail out. Just as he was getting ready to climb over the side of the cockpit, the propeller caught on again. But still, he thought, it could run away again too. Then he remembered

John T. Godfrey (left)
and Don Gentile

Duane W. Beeson (left)
and Don Gentile

the film in his wing cameras which proved that he had two more 109s to his credit. These would add to the total score of the 4th Fighter Group. He headed his malfunctioning Mustang back across the Alps, Germany and the Channel. When he landed he had only six gallons of fuel left—and his valuable combat film.

Lieutenant Duane Beeson had already landed at Debden.

"Get anything today, Bee?" someone asked.

"Yeah, a 109," said Beeson. He asked how the others did.

Everybody knew what was behind his question. Beeson and Gentile were in a scoring duel. Each had had fourteen victories before today. Now Beeson had fifteen. They told him Gentile had shot down a Focke-Wulf. "Good show," said Beeson, trying not to show his disappointment.

Already the Luftwaffe was pulling back and refusing to meet the American fighters. Many Thunderbolts and Mustangs were forced to go "down on the deck"—the ground—and strafe enemy planes. On March 23rd, Gentile and Godfrey teamed up again, and Gentile got two more and then covered Godfrey while he shot down a ME-109.

By the end of March, Gentile had equaled Bob Johnson's score of twenty-two, and Duane Beeson was just behind with twenty-one. Neither Gentile nor Beeson would go to London for a day off for fear the other would pass him. Blakeslee was delighted with the whole group. They had destroyed 156 German planes in one month, a new Eighth Air Force record. The 4th had come alive and was outshooting the Wolf Pack.

But the race between Beeson and Gentile was over five days later. On a low strafing run, Duane Beeson's Mustang was hit by ground fire. What the best pilots in the Luftwaffe couldn't do, a machine gunner who couldn't even fly had finally accomplished. Several other good pilots were lost too, but again the group had hurt the Germans badly. Blakeslee's boys had destroyed fifty enemy planes and damaged another thirty-eight. Gentile got five German planes on the ground that day, bringing his total to twenty-seven.

Gentile was out hunting again on April 8th. Blakeslee led the Group into one of the fiercest fights yet. More than a hundred German planes dropped out of the sun. Gentile directed his squadron in an attack on some thirty enemy fighters after they had made one pass at the bombers the 4th was escorting. He got one . . . then another. He chased a third FW-190 down to the deck among the trees and ravines. He overshot the Focke-Wulf once, then came around, throttle back, and hit him squarely. It was Gentile's twenty-third victory in aerial combat.

In the first eight days of April, the 4th had eliminated seventy-six enemy planes. They couldn't be stopped. Their total score was now 373½ destroyed and the Wolf Pack was no longer so far ahead. Zemke's group had 384.

Blakeslee was jubilant. He predicted, "We're going to bring it up to 500 destroyed by the end of the month!"

F6F HELLCAT

8 The Great Marianas "Turkey Shoot"

The road up through the Solomons and Rabaul in the South Pacific was not the only way to Japan. Across the Central Pacific, like giant stepping stones, lay another set of island groups called the Gilberts, the Marshalls and the Marianas. If you draw a line through these islands toward Japan, you will see that it points directly to Okinawa. And Okinawa is just south of the enemy homeland. The long distances between these islands made it impossible for land-based fighters to take a major part in the bloody campaigns waged to capture them. Of necessity the air war again became a carrier war.

The Navy's pilots were more than ready. They

not only had the experience, but by late 1943 they had a superb new fighter. This was the Grumman F6F Hellcat, the design of which benefited from the Zero captured intact in the Aleutians. The Hellcat was almost as fast as the Marines' Corsair and was more maneuverable. It too could outclimb and outdive the Zero. And it was heavily armed and armored. One pilot, when he noticed the heavy armor plating behind him and the thick, bulletproof wind screen ahead, reported that he felt as if he were sitting in a flying tank. Lieutenant Eugene A. Valencia probably spoke for a great many Navy fighter pilots when he said, "I love this airplane so much that if it could cook I'd marry it."

In November, 1943, United States forces hit Tarawa in the Gilbert Islands. Carrier attacks and shells from our big ships had tried to "soften up" the island, but they had not been very successful. The marines on the beaches fought one of the most bloody and savage battles of the war before Tarawa was taken. At least the marines didn't have to worry about death from the skies. One Hellcat squadron off the *Lexington,* called the "Pistol Packing Airedales," shot down seventeen of the twenty Zeros they encountered without losing one of their own fighters.

It was during this battle for the Gilberts that

the great Butch O'Hare, the savior of the *Lexington,* was accidentally shot down by another American plane on the first successful night-fighter operation from a carrier.

The Marshall Islands were next on the list. American forces invaded them in February, 1944, three months after the bloody battle of Tarawa. This time Admiral R. A. Spruance's Fifth Fleet really pounded the islands, and the landing marines had a little easier time of it. In the meantime Admiral Marc Mitscher's Task Force 58 had gone on ahead to blast Japan's mighty supply de-

pot in the Central Pacific, the island of Truk. Truk was strategically placed between the American two-pronged offensive, and it was heavily fortified. Mitscher had nine carriers and he launched every plane he could at Truk. During a fighter sweep at dawn our Hellcats shot down fifty-six enemy planes and destroyed seventy-two more on the ground. Some pilots like Lieutenant Valencia accounted for three planes each. The Americans lost only four fighters. Unfortunately most of the Japanese Fleet based at Truk escaped.

Though emphasis has generally been placed on air losses from enemy fire, we actually lost a greater number of airplanes from operational accidents. This was true in all theaters, but the circumstances were often more dramatic in the vast and treacherous Pacific. On Guadalcanal, for instance, the conditions were so bad that many pilots lost their planes and even their lives just in landing or taking off. Carrier operations, of course, are always particularly hazardous, and any overwater mission in a single-engine fighter is potentially dangerous. In one case a squadron of Marine Corsairs was being restaged southward from Tarawa to Funafuti, a flight of 700 miles. About halfway to their destination they became lost in a storm. Several dropped out because of engine trouble and lost sight of the others. A few

F6F Hellcats flying in formation

managed to get the correct radio bearings and landed successfully, but fifteen of them, almost out of fuel, decided to ditch in the water together. Thirteen of these pilots floated in rubber rafts for two days before they were picked up. Altogether twenty-two Corsairs were lost and six experienced pilots never came back.

The Fifth Air Force fliers on New Guinea experienced a similar tragedy. On Easter Sunday, 1944, General Kenney sent a large group of planes to raid the Japanese base at Hollandia. There were over 100 bombers and many fighters. On their way back they ran into bad weather, which completely covered their home base near Lae. They were low on fuel and had to try to land through the overcast. Many pilots lost their way and crashed. Others couldn't maintain control of their aircraft in the "soup" and spun out. Altogether thirty-one planes with their crews were lost. General Kenney wrote: "It was the worst blow I took in the whole war."

"The Hellcats Won the Battle"

If the Marianas Islands could be captured, America would have bases which would present an immediate threat to the enemy. From the Marianas our giant Boeing B-29 "Superfortresses"

F6F Hellcat landing on its carrier

could bomb the Japanese homeland only 1200 miles away. The Marianas consist of an island chain almost 400 miles long. At the southern reaches of the chain lie its three largest and most important islands—Saipan, Tinian and Guam.

The Japanese were determined to stop us. The Japanese Premier, Hideki Tojo, said, "The fate of the Empire rests on this one battle." Out from the Philippines sailed Admiral Jisaburo Ozawa with the largest fleet Japan could assemble. Ozawa had nine aircraft carriers, five battleships and many cruisers and destroyers. But to oppose Ozawa, Admiral Spruance had an even greater fleet—Task Force 58 under the direct command of Marc Mitscher. Mitscher had fifteen carriers, seven battleships and over ninety cruisers and destroyers.

Nevertheless Admiral Ozawa had some reason to feel he could be victorious. His planes could fly farther than the American planes, and he thought perhaps he could stay out of reach. He also counted on help from at least 500 land-based planes from the Marianas. He even planned a sort of shuttle operation in which his aircraft would attack the United States task force, fly on to Guam, refuel and rearm, and hit the Americans again on the return trip to the Japanese carriers. He also counted heavily on the element of surprise.

Nothing Ozawa counted on was to work out.

For one thing, untested American pilots were no longer facing experienced Japanese pilots. All our fliers now had at least two years of training—with over 300 flying hours each—before being assigned to carrier duty. The present Japanese pilots had six months' training at most, and some not even that. The Zero was no longer master either, now that the Americans had the Hellcat.

On June 11th, at dusk, we began our attack on

Carriers of Task Force 58 at anchor in Pacific

Saipan. Almost 1,000 planes from Task Force 58 took part in the pre-invasion assault. Not only did they pound the ground defenses, they struck hard at the enemy planes which were to help Ozawa. By the time the 2nd and 4th Marine Divisions had hit the beaches—just a little more than a week after the Allied invasion of France on the other side of the world—there were no more than fifty Japanese planes left on the islands. The marines had a rough time of it—4200 casualties in the first two days—but they held on.

With Ozawa's Japanese fleet bearing down, Mitscher's task force had a double assignment: to stay in place to protect the marines, and to fight—and try to destroy—the determined enemy fleet.

The morning of June 19th was, in pilot's language, CAVU—Ceiling and Visibility Unlimited. It was going to be a big day for Lieutenant Joe Eggert, the task force fighter director aboard the new *Lexington.* It was his job to direct Mitscher's 475 fighter planes. He had to tell them where to go to intercept; he had to hold the right number in reserve, and he had to schedule these complex operations so that landings, take-offs and refuelings would not interfere with each other.

The first action came early, at 6:30 A.M. A combat air patrol discovered a few Japanese planes trying to take off from Orote Field on Guam and gunned them down. A little later at 8:07 thirty-three Hellcats were vectored over Guam again and shot down thirty Zeros and five bombers—thirty-five more planes that would never help Ozawa.

All was quiet for a time, and then at 9:59 the American radar picked up a large "bogie"—enemy planes were approaching. This was Ozawa's Raid I, consisting of sixty-nine Zeros and bombers. General quarters sounded. Mitscher himself called, "Hey, Rube!" over the radio. It was the signal for the fighters over Guam to return to their ships and prepare for battle. At 10:17 "Pilots, man your planes!" blared over the carriers' bull horn. One by one the Hellcats leaped into the sky.

The first to see the enemy was Lieutenant Commander C. W. Brewer, who skippered the *Lexington's* fighters. He rolled over and led his eleven Hellcats into battle. His first victim was a Japanese bomber which exploded. Then he blasted the wing off another and saw it spiral crazily into the sea. A Zero got on Brewer's tail, but he shook it off. Then he got the enemy fighter in his sights and fired. The Zero burst into flame and plunged downward. Almost as quickly Commander Brewer's guns downed still another Zero.

Now Hellcats from other carriers joined the fight. Lieutenant Alexander Vraciu, who had once been O'Hare's wingman, was having engine trouble. He was ordered to drop back, but Vraciu couldn't resist combat. He headed for the raiders. Suddenly he called over his radio, "Tallyho—at least thirty rats [Japanese planes]." They were 2,000 feet below him when he began his dive with the other Hellcats. Almost immediately he shot down three Judy bombers. Lieutenant Vraciu said later the Hellcats were like cowboys on a roundup.

The Japanese seemed to have no plan of battle. When some tried to escape, the Hellcats herded them back into the center where they were more easily attacked. Vraciu, in spite of his engine trouble, got three more that day. The last one exploded so close to him that the concussion sent his Hellcat spinning. After he regained control he radioed back, "Splash Number Six." When he landed eight minutes later he was greeted as the Navy's new top ace with eighteen kills.

Ensign Wilbur "Spider" Webb also downed six enemy planes before the day was over.

Only forty-two of the sixty-nine Japanese planes in Raid I returned. The Americans lost one Hellcat, but its pilot was saved.

Alexander Vraciu (Navy)

Raid II was a bigger one—fifty-three Judy bombers, twenty-seven Jill Torpedo bombers and forty-eight Zeros. On board the *Lexington,* Lieutenant Eggert, in directing the fighter action, discovered he had help from an unexpected source. A Japanese "air coördinator" was circling near the battle area telling his attacking planes where to go. The Americans listened in on his instructions and thereafter knew every enemy move ahead of time.

Commander David McCampbell led his "Fabled Fifteen" squadron to intercept this new raid. Over the radio the *Essex* heard him call, "Nine o'clock down, two miles." At 11:39 his Hellcats bored into the giant enemy formation (by now other fighters had joined him too). McCampbell got a Judy bomber on his first pass. Then facing heavy return fire, he headed into two more. They burst into flames under his accurate shooting. Before the day was over he downed four more. Commander McCampbell was on his way to becoming the Navy's ace-of-aces.

Ensign Bradford Hagie had an unusual experience. He was a new replacement pilot and had landed on the wrong carrier the day before. During the battle he was ordered to ferry his Hellcat back to his own carrier. But he didn't waste the short flight. On the way he shot down three attackers. Altogether thirty-two Zeros, twenty-two

Jills and forty-two Judys didn't return to Ozawa's fleet.

Raid III consisted of forty-seven Japanese aircraft. Forty Hellcats took off after them, but a false radar bearing made them miss most of the formation. Even so, the Japanese did little damage to Mitscher's task force.

Raid IV contained fifty enemy planes. This time they failed completely to contact our fleet, and headed on for Guam. There they were intercepted by Commander Gaylord Brown's combat air patrol. Brown radioed for help: "Forty enemy planes circling Orote Field at Angels three [3,000 feet], some with wheels down." McCampbell came on with seven Hellcats, as did Lieutenant William Blair. They shot down thirty out of forty-nine Japanese planes. The rest were so badly damaged they never flew again.

One of Admiral Mitscher's officers now wanted to shoot down the lone Japanese air coördinator who had been so "helpful" all day. "No indeed!" said Mitscher. "He did us too much good!"

The Turkey Shoot, as it came to be called, was almost over. At dusk Commander Brewer, who had made the first contact that day, was leading a sweep over Orote Field. He dived on a bomber trying to make a sneak landing. Suddenly a hidden formation of Zeros jumped Brewer and his

Men on U.S. carrier near Saipan cheering as a Japanese plane, ablaze from anti-aircraft fire, falls into the water

wingman. Both pilots were killed in the attack.

Japanese losses were astounding. Ozawa had lost 366 planes; we had lost only 26. Mitscher's tactical officer, Commander James H. Hean, summed it up: "The Hellcats won the battle."

Admiral Ozawa's fleet fled the scene of the disaster. The Admiral's own ship had been torpedoed and sunk. Mitscher steamed after the Japanese, but didn't dare go too far because the landings on

Saipan couldn't be left unprotected. Late in the afternoon of the next day, Mitscher launched a counterattack at a great distance. Our bombers and fighters inflicted severe damage on Ozawa's forces, but the long trip home turned into a nightmare.

Over the radio the task force heard the returning pilots talking:

"I've only got a couple of minutes' gas left, Tom. I'm going in while I've still got power. So long."

"Where's somebody? I'm lost."

Untold numbers of aircraft were not going to be able to make it. And those that could were having difficulty finding their carriers in the dark.

Admiral Mitscher made a daring decision. He ordered the lights on his carriers turned on. He knew enemy submarines might be around, but he wanted to save as many of his pilots as he could.

Because of Mitscher's action only thirty-eight pilots lost their lives, but even with this help at least 100 were forced to ditch in the sea.

The greatest carrier battle of the war was over. Shortly thereafter Premier Tojo and his whole cabinet resigned.

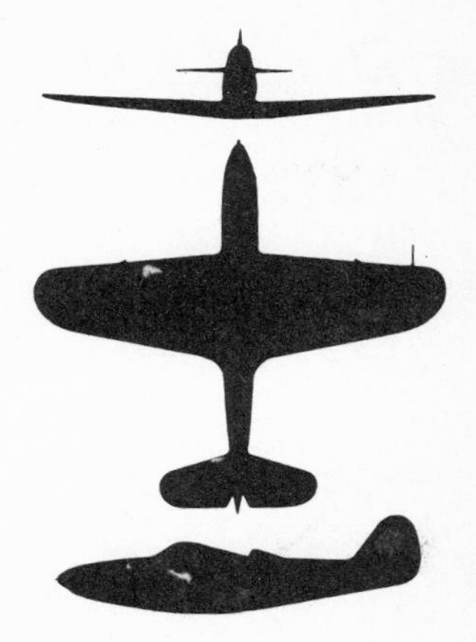

P-39 AIRACOBRA

9 Return to the Philippines

By late 1944 American Pacific military might had grown to almost unbelievable proportions. Admiral William "Bull" Halsey's Third Fleet, for instance, had seventeen carriers as well as hundreds of other ships of all tonnages. And this was by no means all of our naval strength. It was a far cry from the early months of 1942 when only three United States carriers had tried to stem the advance of Japanese sea power.

Now it was time for the most important amphibious landing to date in the Pacific. General MacArthur had sworn to the people of the Philippines that he would return and liberate them. At last he had the men, the ships and the planes to do it. D-Day was set for October 20th.

Umbrella of Hellcats

MacArthur decided that he would hit the Philippines directly in the middle—on the island of Leyte. He knew the Japanese would put up strong resistance. He also knew that if he did not have supremacy in the air the landings would have no assurance of success. But Leyte was too far from Army bases for General Kenney's planes to be of much help. MacArthur had to turn to Halsey's powerful Third Fleet and its carriers.

Admiral Halsey decided the first thing to do was to attack Japanese-held islands to the north. If these enemy bases were hit hard enough they would not be able to send aerial reinforcements when the actual invasion of Leyte began.

On October 10th hundreds of fighters and bombers from Admiral Mitscher's Task Force 38 swarmed over enemy airfields and harbors on Okinawa, destroying everything in sight. Two days later planes from the same carriers hit Formosa, just north of the Philippines. Hundreds of Japanese fighters rose to stop the incoming planes. While our bombers and torpedo planes headed for their targets, the Hellcat escort met the Japanese interceptors head on. One of the great fighter-plane

Admiral William "Bull" Halsey (left)

Cecil E. Harris (Navy)

battles of the war had begun.

Right in the center of the fight was Lieutenant Cecil Harris. Three times during the war, Harris shot down four planes in a single day. This was one of those times. He braved intense anti-aircraft fire to lead his flight to an important airfield. Then, against great odds, he entered a vicious dog-fight in which he not only destroyed four Zeros but saved two of his teammates from certain death. (Two days later Lieutenant Harris shot down three more Zeros while braving heavy defensive fire from American ships. He became the second-ranking Navy ace.)

In the first day over Formosa, American Hellcats knocked down more than 200 Zeros and enemy bombers trying to make a counterattack against Mitscher's task force. It was the beginning

Pilots in the ready room of their aircraft carrier

of the most violent week of aerial fighting in the Pacific. Before it was over we had destroyed 650 enemy planes, and had lost only 89 of our own.

As October 20th drew close, a great American armada formed at sea. From many bases in the Pacific 700 ships converged on the island of Leyte. Even from high in an airplane an observer could not have seen all of the awesome fleet at once. Admiral Thomas Kinkaid's Seventh Fleet was to be the attack force and also shepherd this mammoth convoy which was transporting 193,841 Army troops toward the landing beaches. Halsey's Third Fleet was to stand off and give general support.

Early on the morning of October 20th, planes from Mitscher's carriers as well as Admiral T. L. Sprague's three groups of escort carriers, which were with the landing force, took off for Leyte and other islands in the Philippines. The names of their targets had a familiar ring—Nichols Field, Subic Bay, Clark Field.

A squadron of Hellcats—Fighting 27—from the carrier *Princeton,* couldn't find anything to shoot at over Manila. Tired of waiting Lieutenant Carl Brown decided to light a cigarette. Then Brown saw a large formation of Zeros. "Fred," he yelled over his radio to squadron leader Lieutenant Commander Fred Bardshar. "I see a welcoming committee topside." Although the Hellcats were outnumbered five to one, Bardshar called his fighters together and slashed directly into the Japanese. Planes began to fall from the sky over Manila—thirty-eight in all—and every one of them was Japanese. When it was all over, Brown noticed that not one of the Fighting 27's Hellcats was missing. Then he felt something burn his lips. It was his cigarette. The whole fight had lasted just as long as the cigarette took to burn down. That day the Japanese lost sixty-six planes in the air while only six of ours failed to return.

The landings on Leyte's east coast near Tacloban and Dulag were a success. General MacArthur sailed in with the invasion force aboard the *Nashville.* That afternoon he radioed a message to all the islands: "This is the voice of freedom, General MacArthur speaking. People of the Philippines! I have returned. . . ." A little later he waded ashore and repeated the message from the beach. General Tomoyuki Yamashita, the commander of the Japanese forces, could not believe that MacArthur had actually been brave enough to come ashore so soon. Yamashita said later that if he had been able to believe it he would have concentrated his forces in an attempt to kill MacArthur to avenge Admiral Yamamoto's death.

The Battle of Leyte Gulf

So far things had gone according to plan. But the Japanese had a plan of their own. They were marshaling all of their remaining strength in the air and on the sea for a smashing counterattack that was as daring as it was cunning. The complex scheme called for every available land-based enemy plane to hit our fleets. At the same time our sprawling invasion force in Leyte Gulf was to be attacked by sea from two directions.

Early on October 24th the Americans noticed increased enemy activity in the air. In fact the Japanese actually regained control of the air for a while at a particularly dangerous time. We doubled our combat air patrols and put sixteen Hellcats on alert on each big carrier. It was fortunate we did. Eight pilots from Fighting 27 led by Lieutenant Carl Brown were flying CAP over the carrier *Princeton* when a large "bogie" was reported.

This turned out to be a Japanese attack force of eighty planes, including sixty-five fighters. Brown intercepted the dangerous flight with his few F6Fs. Fighting 27 shot down many of them, but help was needed urgently. One enemy bomber had already broken through and would make a direct hit on the *Princeton.*

Help came in the form of seven more Hellcats from the Fabled Fifteen off the *Essex*. Commander David McCampbell cleared his guns and with his wingman, Lieutenant Roy Rushing, took on

Carrier planes soften up Leyte beachhead

the enemy fighters. On their first pass each shot down one. Immediately McCampbell pulled up, turned and got another Zero.

Then, to McCampbell's and Rushing's amazement, the remaining thirty-seven Japanese formed themselves into a giant Lufbery Circle. This was a formation perfected by an American fighter pilot in World War I. Each plane in the circle had a friendly plane behind it for protection. Commander McCampbell made several passes at the circle but had to withdraw because of the withering return fire. He lit a cigarette and tried to figure a new plan of attack. The Japanese circle was moving toward home, so he had to try something.

He made two daring head-on attacks directly into the Zeros. One fell away in flames. The circle began to break up. The Zeros were retreating toward Manila. McCampbell and Rushing took after them, each downing another plane. (McCampbell now had four, Rushing three.) The two Hellcat pilots would not give up. All alone they continued to attack the larger group. McCampbell got another. Then another. And still another. Rushing too was scoring. There seemed to be no end to the planes falling from the sky. Then, to cap an amazing performance, David McCampbell shot down a ninth plane! Roy Rushing hadn't done badly either; his total score was six.

David S. McCampbell (Navy). The Japanese flags painted on his plane indicate the number of enemy aircraft downed.

Commander McCampbell broke off the engagement only because fuel was running low. He became the Navy's Number One ace, with thirty-four confirmed air-to-air victories.

While this aerial battle was going on, our invasion force was being threatened. Admiral Takeo Kurita was leading a powerful fleet of five battleships, ten heavy cruisers, two light cruisers and many destroyers toward San Bernardino Strait just north of Leyte. American submarines and planes attacked this fleet and turned it back—momentarily. Another Japanese force consisting of two battleships, a cruiser and four destroyers led by Admiral Shoji Nashimura was coming through Surigao Strait just south of Leyte. This enemy formation was met at night by American Admiral Jesse B. Oldendorf's six battleships and eight cruisers. (Many of these battleships had been raised from the bottom of Pearl Harbor.) Admiral Oldendorf performed the classic naval maneuver called "capping the T"—which means that he sailed his ships across the bows of the enemy so that he could fire most of his guns at them while they could only use their forward guns against him. Nashimura was destroyed. It was the last great naval battle in which air power played no part.

But now, unknown to the Americans, Admiral Kurita's strong force was again heading through

San Bernardino Strait. Ordinarily Halsey's gigantic Third Fleet would have been waiting for him, but the Japanese had lured Halsey away. They had sent Admiral Ozawa (who had lost so many planes during the Marianas "Turkey Shoot") to appear with his carriers north of the Philippines. Ozawa had only twenty planes left, but Halsey didn't know this. He only knew that the carriers were a potential danger, and he sent his whole fleet north after them, leaving the Leyte area relatively unprotected.

By the next day Admiral Kurita had gone through San Bernardino Strait and was within three hours of the American Leyte beachhead. All that immediately stood in the way was Admiral Clifford Sprague's "Taffy 3" group of six escort carriers, three destroyers and four destroyer escorts. This force had been giving tactical support to the invasion. These escort carriers (sometimes called "babies" or "jeeps") were slow and carried few planes. Against Kurita's battleships and cruisers they didn't have a chance. But Sprague fought. He sent off all his planes and got help from other jeep carriers in the area. His few destroyers raced toward the enemy fleet and launched torpedos. Then they tried to hide the small carriers with smoke. This destroyer attack under suicide conditions was perhaps the most heroic naval action of the war. Kurita's fleet was hurt slightly and temporarily disorganized. But Sprague paid heavily. He lost two destroyers, a destroyer escort and a jeep carrier, with several more ships badly damaged. The baby flattops had lost 105 planes too. The destruction of MacArthur's invasion force seemed inevitable.

Suddenly Kurita turned his ships back. He had been attacked so aggressively that he thought a much more powerful American force opposed him than actually did. Not only were our Leyte forces safe but now the Japanese naval fleet was being hunted down.

In the north Halsey had found Ozawa's carriers and attacked. Commander McCampbell led the aerial strike as "target coördinator." He stayed over the Japanese carriers for three hours directing the strafing and bombing. Commander Hugh Winters had him beat for endurance, however. He was over the target almost nine hours. He kept hearing Jimmy Flatley and others calling from the *Lexington,* "Get the carriers! Get the carriers!"

Finally Winters in exasperation called back, "They're all going under the water."

He heard laughter from the *Lexington* in his headphones: "That's all we wanted to know!"

Kurita's fleet, now in retreat, was also under attack by sea and by air. By the time the battle was over, Japan had lost most of its sea power—four carriers, three battleships, ten cruisers and many destroyers. Hundreds of her planes had been shot down and almost 10,000 of her seamen were dead. We paid heavily too for the victory. Almost 3,000 Americans lost their lives. Great numbers of our planes were destroyed, as well as several small carriers and destroyers.

We did not yet understand, however, the most ominous event of the battle. Japanese planes had deliberately made suicide dives into our escort carriers, *Santee, Suwannee* and *St. Lo.*

Ace of Aces

There were small Japanese airstrips near Tacloban and Dulag, where MacArthur had landed. General Kenney set about lengthening them for his P-38s immediately. On October 27th at noon the first group of thirty-four Lightnings flew in to their new base.

General MacArthur was visiting Kenney just at that moment. A short, stocky pilot got out of the last P-38. When Kenney saw him he was surprised. He yelled, "Bong, come over here."

Major Richard Bong walked shyly over to Generals MacArthur and Kenney. He knew he shouldn't be at the front. He now had thirty victories and, as a gunnery instructor, he was supposed to stay out of combat.

"Who told you to come up here?" Kenney asked.

"Oh, I got permission from General Whitehead."

Kenney asked him if Whitehead said he could fly combat.

"No," answered Bong, "but can I?"

Everybody, including MacArthur, laughed. Kenney let Bong stay. He needed every P-38 pilot he could get.

That very afternoon Bong took off with three other Lightnings and shot down another Zero. Lieutenant Colonel Gerald R. Johnson, the group's executive officer, got two. The next day Dick Bong's superb marksmanship claimed two more enemy fighters while he was searching for new sites for airfields.

General Kenney immediately wrote a humorous letter to General Arnold, explaining that Bong, who wasn't supposed to be in combat, now had raised his score to thirty-three.

General Arnold answered in kind:

"Major Bong's excuses in matter of shooting down three more Nips noted with happy skepticism by this headquarters."

Tacloban was becoming the busiest airport in

the world. Kenney's P-38s were not the only planes operating from it. Navy planes whose carriers had been lost in the Battle of Leyte Gulf had to use it for a while too. And soon Marine Corsairs and dive bombers would land there.

At the end of October another twenty Lightnings arrived at Tacloban. As they came in to land, ten Japanese planes got in their way and the P-38 pilots shot down six of them. Major Tommy McGuire was one of the new arrivals and he was glad to be at Tacloban. "This is the kind of place I like," he said, "where you have to shoot 'em down so you can land." McGuire now had twenty-five victories. He always seemed to be just eight behind Bong.

All through the month of November Kenney's fighters made sorties against the Japanese defenders. By December Bong's score was thirty-six. McGuire was still right behind with twenty-eight.

The first week in December was crucial. The Japanese had landed fresh troops at Ormac Bay, on the other side of Leyte from Tacloban. Marine night-fighter Corsairs attacked the new threat. And P-38s tried to protect a new landing of American troops near Ormac.

The Fifth Air Force threw every fighter it had at the Japanese. On December 7th Colonel Charles MacDonald, commander of the 475 Fighter Group

General Douglas MacArthur congratulates Richard Bong after awarding him the Congressional Medal of Honor

at Dulag, flew four missions over the Ormac landing. He found no action on his first sortie, but on the second he got on the tail of an enemy fighter who was attacking our ships and chased him in and out of the clouds. Finally MacDonald got him. On his next flight he shot down two more over the same place. Gerald Johnson also got three more victories that day. In all, the Army Lightnings downed sixty-four Japanese planes on this third anniversary of Pearl Harbor.

"Instructor" Dick Bong got into the fight too and destroyed a bomber and a fighter. Tommy McGuire was right alongside Bong and he also shot down two enemy planes.

General Kenney thought it was time Major Bong received the Medal of Honor. With his unmatched record he deserved it if anyone did.

General MacArthur agreed to present the Medal to Dick Bong personally at the Tacloban airstrip. MacArthur had prepared a short speech but he didn't use it. When he stood in front of the young pilot from Wisconsin he simply put his hands on Bong's shoulders and spoke one sentence. General Kenney thought it was the greatest speech he'd ever heard:

"Major Richard Ira Bong, who has ruled the air from New Guinea to the Philippines, I now induct you into the society of the bravest of the brave, the wearers of the Congressional Medal of Honor of the United States."

On the fifteenth of December the two leading fighter pilots in the Pacific, Bong and McGuire, went off together with their wingmen to hunt the Japanese. They couldn't find anything at first. Then McGuire saw two enemy planes. Secretly he signaled to his wingman and attacked. The Japanese plane blew up. McGuire turned to blast the remaining enemy fighter, but Bong beat him to it. Bong flew alongside Tommy McGuire and grinned.

The same thing happened on the 17th. Now

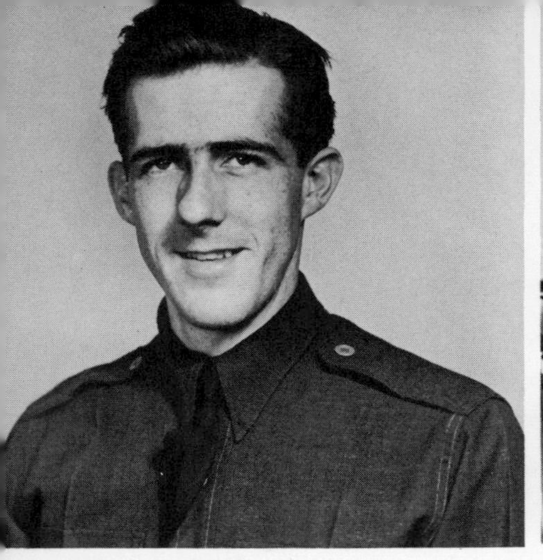

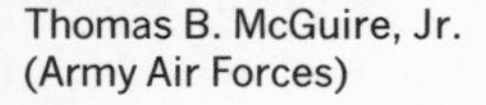

Thomas B. McGuire, Jr.
(Army Air Forces)

William A. Shomo (right) after receiving the Medal of Honor from General Ennis C. Whitehead

Bong's record stood at an incredible forty victories. General Kenney decided it was time to send Dick Bong home—for good. Everybody, including Kenney himself, knew that Bong had shot down at least twice as many enemy planes as he was credited with, but these kills could not be made official because the necessary witnesses weren't always around.

Tommy McGuire came close to equaling Bong's score just shortly after Bong was sent home. While he had the field to himself, McGuire ran his string of victories to thirty-eight before fate struck him down. He killed himself in a high speed stall trying to save a fellow pilot who was under attack.

But Kenney's command continued to perform remarkable feats. Just four days later, on the eleventh of January, 1945, a pilot who had never been in combat before made the whole Fifth Air

Force take notice. The pilot's name was Captain William Shomo and he was flying one of the first of the new P-51 Mustangs to see action in the Pacific. The first indication that something unusual had happened during Captain Shomo's baptism of fire came when he returned to his field and began doing Victory Rolls. He did seven of them. After the first few, the spectators on the ground were excited because they knew these were Shomo's first victories. But as the rolls continued, the onlookers became angry. The Victory Roll was a sacred thing and not to be made fun of.

Shomo's wingman, Lieutenant Paul Lipscomb, landed first and explained to his irate commanders that Shomo really *had* shot down seven planes—one bomber and six new Japanese fighters.

"And not only did he get seven," Lipscomb explained in his Texas drawl, "but Ah got four!"

The officers then asked Lipscomb why he hadn't made any Victory Rolls.

"Well, sir," he answered apologetically, "Ah just got checked out in this plane, and Ah ain't sure Ah know how."

Captain Shomo's seven victories won in a single mission tied Marine Jimmy Swett's remarkable performance over the Solomons many months before. But the most startling circumstance in both instances was the fact that neither had ever fired at another plane before.

No other American pilot ever equaled Richard Bong's record, and none ever will. Bong will remain our ace-of-aces because the days of personal combat in the sky are over. Already guided rockets and automatic vectoring systems are replacing the individual pilot's aerial skills.

There were to be almost three more months of hard, bloody fighting before MacArthur's forces finally recaptured Manila. But the greatest race of the aces was over.

P-51 MUSTANG

10 Down on the Deck

During the months of February and March, 1944, the Luftwaffe lost 800 planes, and most of them fell before the aggressive guns of American fighter pilots. The pilots in the fifteen fighter groups which now composed the Eighth Air Force—plus the fighters in the newly arrived Ninth Air Force —had won control of the air. Once the Allies had control it was vital that they keep it. The coming invasion of Hitler's conquered Europe would be impossible without it.

Fighter pilots also helped break the stalemate in Italy, where the Allied advance had been stopped by the Germans. Thunderbolt fighter-bombers blasted bridges, strafed highways and blew up supply trains behind enemy lines. This was called Operation Strangle, and from the middle of March through June pilots of the Mediterranean Allied Air Forces flew more than 100,000 missions. In central Italy practically all traffic stopped. The German armies were forced to retreat.

The Luftwaffe was retreating too. German fighters still tried to stop our bombers from reaching their strategic targets, but far-ranging Allied fighter sweeps were finding less and less to shoot at in the air. On April 5th, for example, Mustangs flew over Berlin but no German fighters greeted them. They headed for the deck and strafed an air-

A formation of P-47 Thunderbolts, loaded with bombs and extra gas tanks, flying toward their target in northern Italy

drome. Don Gentile shot up five planes that were sitting on the ground; Johnny Godfrey blew up a locomotive and two planes and damaged several more aircraft. Four pilots failed to return. The fighter pilots slowly began to realize that they were entering what was for them the most dangerous period of the war. Airfields were heavily defended and ground gunners were taking a more deadly toll than even the best enemy fliers ever had.

Of course the savage air battles over Europe were by no means ended. Three days later Gentile shot down three more Messerschmitts in a swirling dogfight—bringing his score to thirty.

Then on April 22nd Blakeslee led the 4th on the neatest bounce of his career. Colonel Don was hoping for some action because there were only a few days left in which to fulfill his prediction that 500 German planes would be destroyed before the end of the month. While his Mustangs were orbiting near a bomber formation over Hamm, Germany, John Godfrey's sharp eyes saw something far below.

"Horseback, Horseback!" he called to Blakeslee. "Below us at 4,000 I see three . . . seven . . . nine—there's a million of them!"

The German Fighter Command had scrambled twenty Messerschmitts to intercept the bombers.

"This is Horseback," Blakeslee answered. "I want no plane—I repeat—no plane to attack by himself. We have a perfect bounce. Drop tanks." All the pilots released their external fuel tanks. "Okay, here we go!"

When the Germans saw the Mustangs plummetting toward them, they formed a Lufbery Circle. The P-51 pilots couldn't get in a good shot without becoming good targets themselves. One by one, however, the Messerschmitts tried to break out of the circle. And each plane that attempted it was cut down. Godfrey got two this way and chased a third down so low that it crashed trying to evade his relentless fire. Blakeslee destroyed two, chasing one into the ground just as Godfrey had. Several other Mustang pilots got one apiece, and then the battle became a free-for-all in the haze. It was hard to tell which side was which.

Blakeslee got an idea:

"Horseback here. All Mustangs start orbiting starboard. Anything orbiting port is a 109—shoot 'em!"

Captain Willard Millikan suddenly found himself turning the wrong way. He hauled his Mustang around with all his strength. He was having his best day and he didn't want it spoiled by getting shot down by his own group. Like Duane Beeson, Millikan was an excellent "shooter" and flier,

General Dwight D. Eisenhower presenting the Distinguished Service Cross to Don Gentile, after having similarly decorated Don Blakeslee (right)

though he had once been washed out by the Air Corps and had then proceeded to join the Royal Canadian Air Force. With a perfect deflection shot Millikan had blasted one Messerschmitt out of the dangerous Lufbery Circle; then he exploded another that was on the tail of a Mustang. He spotted a third ME-109 trying to sneak away, and raced after it. The German pulled up in a tight turn—but not tight enough. Millikan's guns blazed again and the 109 half rolled out of control only 1,000 feet above the ground.

Only four of the Messerschmitts escaped. When the group returned, Gentile, who had had an accident a few days before and was forced to stay home, was frantic. "Gee, save me some, will you, fellas?"

But Don Gentile had shot down his last German plane. Now the top fighter pilot in the ETO, he was ordered home for a rest. Johnny Godfrey, his wingman, was sent back to America with him. Neither wanted to go, but at least they had the satisfaction of knowing that they had played a major role in building up the tremendous reputation of the 4th Fighter Group. By April 28th the 4th had destroyed 207 enemy planes in one month —a new record—and had passed Blakeslee's goal of 500.

Like the 4th, Zemke's Wolf Pack was finding it harder and harder to meet up with the enemy in the air. Good fliers like Jerry Johnson and Bud Mahurin had been lost "down on the deck." Bob Johnson, however, had been having better luck. His score was now up to twenty-five, but he had only a few hours of combat time left before he too would be sent home. On May 8th he started to turn back from a mission when his motor began to run rough. Then he saw that the B-17s he was escorting were under attack. He didn't hesitate. "The bombers are being hit," he yelled into his mike. "Let's go get 'em!"

Throttles wide open, the big Thunderbolts raced toward the fight. Johnson saw a Messerschmitt coming through the bomber formation. He hauled his P-47 around after it. The 109 tried to turn away but Johnson chopped his power, skidded inside the turn and fired. The Messerschmitt's wing flew off. Johnson then zoomed back into the general battle. Suddenly he saw three Focke-Wulfs closing in on two of his own squadron. "Turn tight left and climb," he called. At the same time he kicked his P-47 toward the enemy leader, forcing the 190 to break off its attack. Then Johnson lined up the second 190. As his bullets hit its cockpit, the plane fell away out of control.

Johnson was jubilant. With twenty-seven victories he'd beaten Eddie Rickenbacker's World War I record. When Johnson got back to base, Hub Zemke met him with a grin. "Get out of here, Johnson," he said proudly. "You're going home!"

June 6, 1944—Invasion!

All the fighter squadrons knew it was going to happen soon, but the exact date was a mystery. Then one day early in June all fighter bases were suddenly closed off from the world. No one could contact anyone outside. Civilians at the bases weren't even allowed to call their families to let them know why they couldn't come home.

Mustangs and Thunderbolts were painted with three broad white stripes around their wings and fuselages (this was to identify them as friendly in the confusion of a great invasion). Early on the morning of June 6th, 6,483 Allied ships headed across the English Channel toward France. The fighters of the Eighth Air Force were to form a protective aerial wall to prevent the Luftwaffe from reaching the landing areas. In case any German planes broke through, the Ninth was to maintain a fighter umbrella over the beaches.

The fighter pilots were sure the Germans would at last be forced to send out all their air strength to try to stop the great invasion. Before the 4th Fighter Group taxied out in the dark that morning at Debden, Blakeslee told his pilots, "I am prepared to lose the whole group." He meant: Stop the German aerial counterattack or don't come back.

Neither Blakeslee nor Zemke—or any of the other fighter group commanders—realized as yet what a superb job they had done in clearing the Germans from the skies. The 4th flew three missions on D-Day but met practically no enemy planes. They dropped bombs on troop trains and vital bridges, but the Luftwaffe simply didn't have the strength to hold back the invasion. Within a week Ninth Air Force fighters were operating in strength from new landing strips in France. After the war Hermann Goering said: "Without the American Air Force, the war would still be going on elsewhere, but certainly not on German soil."

Most of our fighter pilots were disgusted. They

were itching for a fight but nothing happened. Nevertheless they continued to attack the Germans on the ground, even though losses were heavy. Jimmy Goodson, who had saved Blakeslee's life earlier in the war, was hit by flak while strafing an airdrome. A master at low-level attack, Goodson was known as the King of the Strafers. Before he crash-landed his Mustang he called out encouragingly over his radio: "Good-by, boys. Keep up the good work."

As if to ease their disappointment over D-Day, Blakeslee's group was assigned to one of the most exciting and unusual fighter missions of the war. Early on the longest day of the year, June 21st, Blakeslee came into the briefing room wearing, for the first time, a white scarf around his neck. He told his pilots they had been picked to fly the first long-range escort to Russia. They would prove to the Germans that American bombers could shuttle between Russia and England with fighter protection.

"Now look," Blakeslee said, "before we get all excited about it, I'll say the whole trip will take about seven and a half hours. We've done 'em that long before." They weren't to fight on the way over—the trip was too long—and fuel had to be conserved carefully. "No one will take a gun. If you're forced down—a gun is a death warrant."

Then in typical Blakeslee style he added, "No one will abort [turn back] because of lack of oxygen. You'll be at 15,000 feet. You have no business in the 4th if you have to use oxygen at 15,000 feet." Actually the pilots knew that oxygen was usually necessary over 10,000 feet but Colonel Don's iron confidence convinced them they could do just what he said.

The flight was a long one, but Blakeslee led them over the thousands of miles without a mistake. He plotted their course over the unknown with nineteen charts crammed into his small cockpit. Sixty-seven of the sixty-eight Mustangs which began the record flight arrived safely in Russia, a remarkable achievement. Colonel Blakeslee went to Moscow a hero.

The 4th headed home by way of Italy, where they paused briefly to escort Fifteenth Air Force bombers on a mission to Budapest, Hungary. They destroyed German fighters wherever they found them, but lost a few of their own too. One of the best pilots who didn't come back was Kid Hofer. The Kid, who had once brought his damaged Mustang back to base just to save his combat film for his group, was often called "the last of the screwball pilots." He knew no fear and constantly went off on his own to search out a fight. Like Blakeslee he thought that flying fighter planes was

General William E. Kepner (right) greeting Don Blakeslee upon his return to England after flying the first long-range escort to Russia

a "grand sport." The 4th missed him.

During the month of July the Fifteenth Air Force lost more men than all the Allied armies fighting in Italy.

It was in July too that Gabby Gabreski, who had more air-to-air victories than any other American fighter pilot in the ETO, was downed. He was flying his last mission before returning home on leave. While leading his squadron in a strafing attack near Coblenz, he flew so low that his propeller chewed into a slight rise in the field. His heavy Thunderbolt lurched into the ground at 200 miles an hour. He was captured by German farmers and taken to a prison camp.

The Final Push

In the middle of August, 1944, the Allies opened up a new front against Hitler's Fortress Europe. They made strong landings on the southern coast of France, and began squeezing the Nazi armies back toward Germany.

Earlier in the month Major John Godfrey had arrived back at Debden from his enforced leave in the United States. The "Damon and Pythias" team of Gentile and Godfrey had destroyed fifty-six enemy planes. Now Godfrey intended to knock out fifty all by himself. On his first mission after a three-month leave, he destroyed eight railroad trains, strafed an airfield and shattered three JU-52s (one exploded directly underneath him). On the way back he shot down an ME-109 only 200 feet above the streets of Hanover, Germany. His score of thirty (seventeen in the air, thirteen on the ground) now equaled Gentile's; but he was shaken when he looked at his Mustang after he landed. It was full of bullet holes and the bottom of the plane was scorched black.

On his next mission Godfrey almost didn't return. After he blasted a twin-engined Messerschmitt out of the sky, he began to strafe another airdrome. He was hit by flak, which knocked out his cooling system. Godfrey pulled up to 2,000 feet and radioed that he'd have to bail out. Major Fred Glover called back sharply: "Don't jump, Johnny!" Glover told him to begin pumping his primer handle and force raw gasoline directly into the engine cylinders. The raw gas wouldn't burn so fast. As a result the engine stayed cool enough to bring Godfrey back to England, though his hand was gouged through to the bone from pumping the primer all the way.

Every day the fighter pilots had to go down on the deck to find targets. On one mission the 4th shot up eighty-eight locomotives, twenty-four box cars, five trucks, thirty-five oil-tank cars, two roundhouses and a train load of buzz bombs on their way to launching sites.

On August 24th Johnny Godfrey made four low-level passes over a German airdrome. Enemy planes were left burning from one end of the field to the other, but Godfrey couldn't stop. On the fifth pass his Mustang was hit and crashed into the ground. Godfrey managed to get out but was captured. A short time later he escaped and made his way back to England. There he discovered that he'd been accidentally shot down by his own wingman who had followed too closely behind

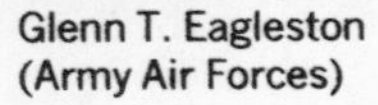
Glenn T. Eagleston
(Army Air Forces)

John T. Godfrey
(Army Air Forces)

Godfrey's P-51.

The Germans continued to manufacture fighter planes at an astounding rate—at least 4,000 were made in September alone. But relentless Allied bombing attacks had robbed the enemy of the vital gasoline to fly these fighters. By this time, too, the remarkable Messerschmitt 262 jet fighter, the first in the war, had made its appearance. It had a top speed of over 500 miles an hour and it could have challenged our air superiority. Luckily Hitler insisted it be used as a tactical fighter-bomber mainly against ground targets.

Once in a while the Germans still tried to meet fighter with fighter. In September Lieutenant Glenn Eagleston, the top ace in the Ninth Air Force, was leading his 354th Fighter Group deep into Germany on a strafing mission when he was bounced by more than 100 ME-109s. Skillfully

Eagleston maneuvered his Mustangs against the superior enemy force and turned the tables. Eagleston flamed three 109s himself and his pilots took care of twenty more, losing only one of their own.

The following month Colonel Hub Zemke's luck ran out. Ice formed on his wings and he couldn't keep his Mustang flying. He had to make a forced landing behind the German lines. When he was taken to a prison camp, the Germans were delighted to see him. "Ah! Colonel Zemke," they said. "Now when we get old Blakeslee the war will be over." As soon as American headquarters in England learned that Zemke was down, Don Blakeslee was grounded. The two greatest fighter commanders in Europe would fight no more.

In November Captain John Voll, the Fifteenth Air Force's leading ace, returned from a memorable fight. Alone over Italy he closed in on a JU-88 when suddenly he was bounced by 7 FW-190s and 5 ME-109s. It was thirteen to one. Voll quickly blasted the JU-88 and turned into his attackers. The Germans, who thought Voll would be an easy kill, later wished they had never seen him. Captain Voll blew up one Focke-Wulf and then another. Then he exploded a Messerschmitt and damaged several more. The Germans were so disrupted that Voll was able to get away. In an earlier fight Voll's unusual skill enabled him to destroy three enemy planes without even firing a shot at them. He tricked two of them into crashing into one another, and then recklessly lured a

John C. Meyer
(Army Air Forces)

George E. Preddy
(Army Air Forces)

third into a power dive toward the ground. Voll pulled out, the German couldn't.

But all the top scorers weren't as fortunate as Eagleston or Voll. Major George Preddy, a veteran of the Pacific war who shot down six German fighters in one day above Hamburg, was killed by our own anti-aircraft gunners as he attacked a Focke-Wulf over Belgium. The same day Colonel John Meyer became the leading European ace when he flamed two Messerschmitts to bring his score to thirty-two. A week later, however, he had a close call. His squadron was attacked by fifty enemy fighters just as it was taking off. The Germans were throwing everything they had at the Allies in a last attempt to hurl them back. Colonel Meyer, who had scarcely finished his take-off, turned his slow-moving Mustang into the German leader and fired. The Messerschmitt fell. Meyer's squadron, inspired by his fighting example, took the offensive. In the snarling dogfight which followed they not only broke up the attack on their field but also destroyed twenty-three of the enemy fighters.

The Luftwaffe was now almost completely knocked out. But American fliers had paid the price. New pilots were constantly needed to replace those lost in combat or returned to the States after long service. In January, 1945, Colonel Schilling of the 56th discovered a disconcerting fact about the famous group. A year earlier the 56th had had twenty-two aces—now it had only one. German flak had accounted for all but one of those shot down.

Still the race for leadership between the 4th and 56th Fighter Groups continued. Both were nearing a total of 1,000 destroyed. Each hunted down the enemy with aggressive determination. Captain Kendall "Swede" Carlson wouldn't quit even when his Mustang crashed after strafing an airdrome. "Hey, Mac," he radioed to Major Pierce Mc-

Kennon who was leading the group, "get those 109s! Get 'em!"

"I don't see them," McKennon called back. "What's your altitude?"

"Altitude?" yelled the excited Carlson. "I haven't got any altitude. I'm on the ground!" Then the Swede stood up in his cockpit and proceeded to direct the rest of the group as they strafed ME-109s trying to land near by. A little later McKennon was shot down near Berlin and Lieutenant George Green, against orders, landed his Mustang in a field near the crashed McKennon. Green removed his parachute, sat his commander in his lap, and took off again, barely clearing the high trees. They both got back to Debden.

The Germans became desperate. Three hundred pilots were selected from the Luftwaffe and trained to ram American bombers with their Focke-Wulfs and Messerschmitts. On April 7th, these suicide fighters rose to meet 1300 Eighth Air Force bombers. The German pilots could not talk because the radio transmitter had been removed from their planes, but patriotic music was broadcast to them. The desperate gamble was a failure. Most of the rammers were shot down. In the two weeks that followed, the Eighth and Ninth Air Forces destroyed 3,484 German aircraft in the air and on the

A B-24 Liberator flying out of a flak barrage over Vienna

ground. The Luftwaffe was no more.

In these last few weeks, the 56th Fighter Group again edged ahead of the 4th. When the war in Europe ended on May 7, 1945, the 56th led by 14½ planes. The fliers in the 4th were crestfallen. They even wished the war could continue for a few more days to give them a chance to catch up.

Then fate took a strange turn. Lieutenant Colonel Sidney Woods, who had been shot down with several other members of the 4th on a strafing mission on April 16th, was freed from his German prison camp by General George Patton's tanks. He and the others downed in his squadron brought back claims for fifteen additional destroyed!

The final, official score: The 4th Fighter Group, 1006½; the 56th Fighter Group, 1006.

But the last act of the war was yet to be played. Halfway around the world Japan was making plans for the most fanatic and deadly resistance in history.

F4U CORSAIR

11 Okinawa: The Desperate Stand

In the middle of the island chain which reaches southwest from Japan to Formosa lies an island sixty miles long named Okinawa. It was only about fifty miles away from the enemy homeland. The American forces needed it as a base from which to launch their final attacks.

After the Battle of Leyte Gulf Japan's sea power was practically nonexistent. Most of her best pilots had been lost in the hundreds of thousands of air battles across the vast Pacific. Japanese aeronautical engineers had designed new fighter types to replace the famous Zero, but these planes were too few and too late.

Yet the coming battle for Okinawa was to be

the biggest and costliest single military operation of World War II, for the Japanese suddenly introduced their most effective air weapon. It was a weapon we could not use. It was called the Kamikaze. In Japanese this meant "divine wind," a name inspired by a great storm which destroyed a fleet of ships trying to invade Japan centuries before.

The Kamikaze was a suicide plane. The pilot pledged to hurl himself, his plane and the bomb it carried against the American ships which threatened Japan. The Japanese soldier had always been trained to fight until death. He was never to surrender. Now the Japanese pilot was asked to fly to certain death. There were thousands of "volunteers." Every type of plane was used—fighters, bombers, observation ships, even trainers. But again the Zero could best bring success to the plan. Its speed and maneuverability would give it a chance to break through American defenses.

From the beginning, the success of the Kamikazes was horrifying. In the month following the American invasion of the Philippines, the "Divine Wind" struck no less than forty American ships—sixteen of them valuable carriers. (In the ten months before Japan surrendered, Kamikaze attacks accounted for almost half of all the United States warships damaged during the whole war.)

Understandably there was grave concern in the Navy. The men on our ships now had to fight for their lives against an enemy who was determined to lose his.

The Navy knew that even the most accurate anti-aircraft fire from its ships could not stop a

F4U Corsair near Okinawa during the invasion

mass Kamikaze attack. The number of fighters aboard our carriers had to be increased immediately, but the Navy could not supply them in time. Thus at last the marines and their Corsairs got a chance at carrier duty. Ten squadrons of F4Us were hastily assigned to sea duty.

Marine pilots began learning the complex operation of carrier flying. They soon learned that

Two photographs showing the actual crash of a Japanese suicide bomber on an aircraft carrier

fighter planes were called "chickens," and they became used to the dramatic cry of the bull horn: "Pilots, man your planes!" Corsairs, now qualified for carrier duty, swept off the narrow, pitching decks. And after a mission the Marine pilots followed the routine of the Navy pilots. As each Corsair landed and taxied past the ship's bridge, its pilot would hold up a finger for each enemy plane he shot down. Then he would hand-signal a radioman on the deck as to whether or not his radio was operating correctly. Next he signaled his squadron engineer about the condition of the plane itself. If anything was wrong, immediate steps were taken to repair the damage.

But carrier duty could not be learned overnight. In January, 1945, the squadrons aboard the *Essex* lost thirteen Corsairs during their first nine days of operation. The weather was particularly bad, but lack of experience was the basic problem.

Just ten days later, however, the marines were able to take part in the landings on Iwo Jima, a small island between Japan and the American bomber base on Saipan. (The United States needed it as an emergency base for B-29s.) Strangely enough this was the first time in the war that Marine Corps fliers had directly supported their fellow marines on the ground during an invasion.

The Invasion of Okinawa

On April 1st a tremendous force of almost 1500 ships began the last and greatest amphibious landing of the war. For weeks Navy and Marine fliers had been "softening up" Okinawa. The actual landing was relatively easy. But the Japanese commander, Mitsuru Ushijima, had concentrated most of his troops in the southern part of the island for a fight-to-the-death stand.

The only effective weapon Japan had left to use against our ships and beachhead was the Kamikaze. A week after the American landing, 355 suicide planes were sent to destroy Admiral Nimitz' fleet, and Task Force 58 in particular. Hellcats and Corsairs met them head on. Very few of the "Divine Wind" pilots even attempted evasion tactics. No less than 288 Kamikazes were destroyed in the air by our carrier fighters and another 39 by ships' anti-aircraft fire. But twenty-two got through and every single one hit a ship.

On April 11th another large wave of Kamikazes was sent out, this time to try to destroy the line of radar picket ships guarding the fleet. There were over a hundred of these ships. But the F4U pilots showed they had learned their trade. They flew until they were literally out of ammunition and gas. Before the day was over the marines from the *Bennington* and the *Bunker Hill* had accounted for almost half the raiders.

During these Kamikaze attacks and the ones which followed, one division of Navy Hellcats (a division was a four-plane fighting unit) set a record—fifty enemy planes shot down with no losses to themselves. This division was based on the *Yorktown* and was trained and led by Lieutenant Eugene Valencia, who became the Navy's third-ranking ace.

Valencia had already destroyed seven Japanese planes on his first tour of duty, and he had formed definite ideas about combat. He was determined "to form a team of fighter pilots who would carry the fight to the Jap, instead of the reverse." He emphasized teamwork. Under Valencia's guidance the four pilots flew constantly to perfect their tactics. At times they even misap-

Eugene A. Valencia (left) and members of his division—Harris E. Mitchell, Clinton L. Smith & James B. French (all Navy pilots)—holding a scoreboard that represents fifty enemy planes shot down

propriated fuel in order to be able to fly more often.

On February 17th Valencia's division had met Japanese Zeros for the first time. Together they downed six. Valencia had known his men were ready, but now they had proved it. When the Kamikaze pilots struck, the new fighter team really showed what it could do.

On April 11th the division was in the vanguard, and Valencia personally exploded three. But it was on April 17th that the division had its greatest day. Thirty-eight enemy planes, including the newest types of fighters as well as Kamikaze planes, were reported heading for the *Yorktown.* Valencia and his pilots engaged the Japanese and remained on the offensive until they personally accounted for fourteen of the enemy. In this battle Valencia got six, James French got four, Harris Mitchell flamed three, and Clinton Smith shot down one.

By the end of the war, every man in the division would be an ace. Valencia believed in letting each pilot have a chance. He wrote later that "during routine combat patrols over the task force, when vectored into singles or doubles (one or two enemy planes), the man having the lowest score, usually Number 4 man, would be given the privilege of making the kill."

A squadron of young Marine pilots known as the "Death Rattlers" was making a name for itself too. During a Kamikaze attack on April 22nd, seven of the Death Rattlers intercepted thirty-nine Zeros and bombers over the China Sea. Three marines who had never shot down a plane before became aces during the fight that followed. When Lieutenant Jerry O'Keefe hit his fifth bomber it tried to ram him. Luckily it exploded only fifty feet away. Major Jefferson Dorroh got six, and Major George Axtell, Jr., who was probably the youngest Marine fighter skipper of World War II, downed five in only fifteen minutes. In just two months Axtell led his "deadly passel of kids" to a new record in the Marine Corps. The Death Rattlers shot down 124 Japanese planes without losing a single one of their own in combat.

Another member of the Death Rattlers, Lieutenant Dewey Durnford, was one of the first to see a new and deadly Japanese suicide plane. It looked like a large torpedo with short, stubby wings. It was powered by a small rocket charge but couldn't really fly. It had to be dropped near the target by a bomber and then guided by its pilot. The Americans called them "Bakas" (fools). When Durnford saw a Betty bomber release its Baka, he yelled into his radio, "Look, you guys, it was carrying a papoose!"

The Kamikazes kept coming. On the night of April 27th, 115 raced toward the United States fleet, accompanied by fighter escort. Hellcats destroyed seventy-four and anti-aircraft fire got thirty more. The next day the Japanese came on again. This time both land- and carrier-based fighters intercepted and thirty-three Kamikazes fell. In many cases American fighter pilots had to follow the Divine Wind pilots right into American anti-aircraft fire. It was a dangerous business but the Corsairs and Hellcats never turned away. The fighter pilots knew that the fate of Admiral Nimitz' fleet was in their hands.

The Japanese sent almost 2,000 Kamikazes at the Americans during the Okinawa campaign. Two hundred and seventy-nine United States ships suffered direct hits. Bad as this was, it could have been a holocaust without aggressive fighter defense.

The tenacity of the fighter pilots over Okinawa is best illustrated by the remarkable story of Marine Lieutenant Robert Klingman. Bob Klingman and his wingman discovered a Japanese plane on a photo-reconnaissance mission high overhead. At 35,000 feet they jettisoned extra fuel to make their F4Us as light as possible. They also fired their guns periodically to try to keep them from freezing. At 38,000 feet Klingman's fellow pilot got off a last burst at the enemy plane but damaged it only slightly. Now all three aircraft were weaving sluggishly, barely able to remain in control in the thin air. Klingman struggled to within fifty feet of the Japanese plane and pressed his gun button. Nothing happened. His guns had frozen. But he was determined not to let the enemy get away. He decided to buzz-saw the fleeing plane. On his first pass he cut off part of his foe's rudder. Then Klingman rammed him again, this time cutting his rudder completely off and part of the stabilizer too—but the reconnaissance plane would not fall. Klingman, more determined than ever, slashed

 A burning Kamikaze just about to crash into a U.S. aircraft carrier

once more at the tail of the Japanese plane. This time he chopped it off completely. The enemy spun down, down, down into the sea. Bob Klingman got back safely, but he had to land deadstick (out of gas) and with part of his propeller gone. His Corsair was full of bullet holes from the rear gun of the plane he had so bravely attacked.

In late June Okinawa surrendered, and American heavy bombers began to blast the Japanese homeland daily. The battle for Okinawa had shown one thing beyond all doubt: an actual invasion of Japan itself would cost the lives of many thousands of Americans. Japan was preparing 10,000 Kamikaze planes, half of them Zeros. They intended to send waves of Divine Wind planes—350 every hour—to destroy the United States fleets.

But we too had a new weapon, one of the greatest technological achievements of the twentieth century. It was the atomic bomb.

On August 6, 1945, a B-29 bomber named *Enola Gay* dropped the first such bomb on Hiroshima. Three days later another atomic bomb was dropped on Nagasaki. The Japanese surrendered.

The American fighter pilot had fought a war which ranged over most of the seas and continents of the world. He was not cut to any one pattern or mold. Some were technicians like Duane Bee-

T. H. Reidy, last man of his naval squadron to get an enemy plane on the day the Japanese surrendered, tells his story to a group aboard the USS Essex

son, who braced his elbows against the sides of his Mustang to perfect his deflection shots. Some like Tommy McGuire fought with a reckless desire for victory. Others like Gene Valencia made teamwork pay off better than it had ever paid off before. And, of course, there were iron men like Don Blakeslee and Joe Bauer, who seemed to live for combat.

All the outstanding pilots had one thing in common, however, and that was the will to fight. "A good fighter pilot," said John Godfrey, "must have one outstanding trait—aggressiveness. Without that he's of no use to his squadron or the Air Force."

The fighter pilot also loved to be first. American fighters had been the first to engage the Japanese in direct combat. Now that the war was over, the big question was: who would be the first to set foot on the Japanese homeland?

Okinawa was jammed with generals, admirals and top-ranking civilians. All of them were eager to be the first to arrive as conquerors of the land they had fought against for so many years. Strict orders were given to all units to stay clear of Japan, but one week after the atomic bomb leveled Nagasaki two P-38s glided into an airfield near Tokyo. Their pilots gave the excuse that they had simply run low on fuel. Excitedly they climbed out of their Lightnings and were greeted courteously by the Japanese operations officer, who bowed and explained that "the war wasn't over yet."

The two American planes were gassed up again and the fighter pilots were given chewing gum and little packages of cigarettes—obviously from GI K-rations.

The P-38s took off, but once they were in the air again the fliers had a good laugh. They had been the first victors on Japanese soil, and nothing anybody else might do could change that. You had to get up pretty early in the morning to be ahead of an American fighter pilot.

PHOTOGRAPH CREDITS:

Bell Aircraft Corporation—page 43 (lower left); European Picture Service—page 77 (lower left); Lockheed Aircraft Corporation—page 43 (upper left); National Archives—pages 7, 44, 166 (left); United Press— pages 164, 192, 199; U. S. Air Force—pages 8, 23, 43 (right), 52 (center & bottom), 55, 59, 67, 70, 74, 77 (top), 81, 85, 86, 91, 107 (left), 109, 111 (right), 115, 117, 122, 127, 129, 131, 166 (right), 170, 173, 179, 182, 184, 187; U. S. Navy—pages 5, 10, 20, 26, 28, 33, 34, 41, 63, 65, 77 (lower right), 89, 93, 95, 96, 100, 105, 107 (right), 111 (left), 136, 139, 141, 144, 147, 151, 152, 155, 157, 191, 195, 201; Wide World—page 52 (top)

Index

If the fighter pilot is an ace, the number in brackets after his name indicates his official air-to-air victories.

27870
LM
R